RECEIVED

2 0 MAR 2010

Moreton Morrell Site

KT-568-819

580
HIL
(D2L)

PLANT SCIENCE

This book is to be returned on or
before the last date stamped
below.
You may b

WITHDRAWN WARWICKSHIRE
COLLEGE
LIBRARY

Dennis Hill-Cottingham

B.Sc., M.Sc., Ph.D.
Principal Scientific Officer, Long Ashton
Research Station, Bristol

&

Pat Hill-Cottingham

B.Sc., C.Biol., M.I.Biol.
Ecological Consultant; Formerly Head of Biology,
Blackwell School, Avon

00074964

Nelson

Thomas Nelson and Sons Ltd
Nelson House Mayfield Road
Walton-on-Thames Surrey
KT12 5PL UK

© Dennis and Pat Hill-Cottingham 1993
Illustrated by David Gardner

First published by Thomas Nelson and Sons Ltd 1993

ISBN 0-17-448198-5
NPN 9 8 7 6 5 4 3

All rights reserved. No part of this publication may be
reproduced, copied or transmitted save with written
permission or in accordance with the provisions of the
Copyright, Design and Patents Act 1988, or under the
terms of any licence permitting limited copying issued by
the Copyright Licensing Agency, 90 Tottenham Court Road,
London W1P 9HE.

Any person who does any unauthorised act in relation to
this publication may be liable to criminal prosecution and
civil claims for damages.

Printed in China

WARWICKSHIRE COLLEGE
LIBRARY

Class No:
580

Acc No:
000 74964

ACKNOWLEDGEMENTS

Photographic material

Graham Burns Photography p.1, p.17 (top), p.75,
p.78 (top right and bottom right), p.80 (bottom
left), p.94 (top left and bottom left)
Frank Lane Picture Agency p.41 (top left), p.56
(bottom right), p.78 (left), p.80 (bottom right), p.86
(bottom right), p.94 (top right)
Science Photo Library p.42, p.43 (top, middle and
bottom), p.55, p.77, p.84, p.86 (top left and top
right), p.89 (top, middle and bottom), p.91 (top and
bottom), p.93, p.95 (bottom left and top right) and
p.97

Cover photograph courtesy of Science Photo
Library

Any photograph not acknowledged is the
copyright of the authors.

The authors would like to acknowledge the invalu-
able help of Richard Pring, Long Ashton Research
Station, who produced all the electron micrographs
shown in the book. We would also like to acknowledge the work of two truly inspiring teachers,
Doreen Cleland and David Etherington, without
whose skill and infectious enthusiasm the world
may never have developed to become so all-
absorbing.

CONTENTS

WARWICKSHIRE
COLLEGE
LIBRARY

General Editor's Introduction to the Series

Biology - Advanced Studies is a series of modular textbooks which are intended for students following advanced courses in biological subjects. The series offers the flexibility essential for working on modern syllabuses which often have core material and option topics. In particular, the books should be very useful for the new modular science courses which are emerging at A-Level.

In most of the titles in the series, one of the authors is a very experienced teacher (often also an examiner) and is sympathetic to the problems of learning at this level. The second author usually has research experience and is familiar with the subject at a higher level. In addition, several members of the writing team have been closely involved in the development of the latest syllabuses.

As with all textbooks, the reader may expect not to read from cover to cover but to study one topic at a time, or dip-in for information as needed. The index can be used like a science dictionary because where a page number is shown in bold print an explanation or definition will be found in the text. Where questions are asked, an attempt should be made at an answer because this type of active reading is the best way to develop an understanding of what is read.

We have referred throughout to Biological nomenclature - Recommendations on terms, units and symbols, Institute of Biology, London, 1989. We are delighted to be able to thank the many friends and colleagues who have helped with original ideas, the reading of drafts and the supply of illustrations.

Alan Cadogan
General Editor

WARWICKSHIRE COLLEGE LIBRARY

Class No: 580

Acc No: 00074964

Authors' Introduction to Plant Science

Our aim has been to make this book a little different from other text books, highlighting the importance of plants in life on earth rather than the more usual step-by-step progression through plant systems. We wanted to include, not just basic standard botany but also the topics that are included in A and AS Level Social Applied Biology syllabuses. You will find, for example, the origin of tillers in wheat, the germination of barley, and even a mention of E-numbers! The diagrams are the result of many years teaching experience in presenting essential information quickly and easily. All the drawings are of actual living specimens; those illustrating germination, for example, are done from material grown especially for this purpose, to avoid the perpetuation of mistakes found in some older botany books. The scanning electron micrograph prints included, help to give a better understanding of morphology; students are advised to study these carefully in relation to their own microscopic work.

Starting to learn a subject like Botany at this level involves mastering a new language. All scientists use specialist terms. This has the advantage of brevity and international acceptibility. Terms are defined as they are introduced with derivations to help you understand them.

We have included, in the index, the scientific names of plants and animals referred to in the text, (including those you are likely to come across on microslide labels!). The vernacular names can vary from one part of Britain to another, whereas scientific names are universally recognised. As a reference book for common, or vernacular, names we have used *English Names of Wild Flowers* by Dony, Jury and Perring (Botanical Society of the British Isles, 2nd ed. 1986).

We hope that you will enjoy delving into this book and, as a result, find that plants are just as fascinating as animals. Not only can we derive endless pleasure from the beauty of plants around us but, even more importantly, they are vital to the survival of the entire animal kingdom.

Dennis and Pat Hill-Cottingham

THE ESSENTIAL PLANT

A wedge from a giant redwood

This huge slice of the trunk of a giant redwood tree is an amazing historical record. It traces over 500 years of history and so could span the time between the printing of the very first book and this one! (Fig.1.1). Later (page 16) you will find the explanation of the biology of rings in the wood of a tree.

Plant science - botany - investigates not only the most massive of living things like the redwood tree but also some microscopic organisms. In this book we will study some of the most unusual plants, some common plants, weed plants, crop plants, those which provide us with shelter and raw materials and those whose influence on our environment make them worthy of our attention and conservation.

Most of us are confident that we can recognise a plant; the house plant on the window-sill, the grass on the lawn, the mosses carpeting a rock and the ferns by a shady stream. These and the products on sale in the greengrocer's shop are familiar members of the plant kingdom and share common characteristics.

What is a plant? From your earlier studies you may recall that most plants are green because they have a green pigment, a chemical called *chlorophyll,* and are able to turn the carbon dioxide from the air into carbohydrates by the process of photosynthesis. So we say that plants are *autotrophic,* they do not need to have ready-made food as we

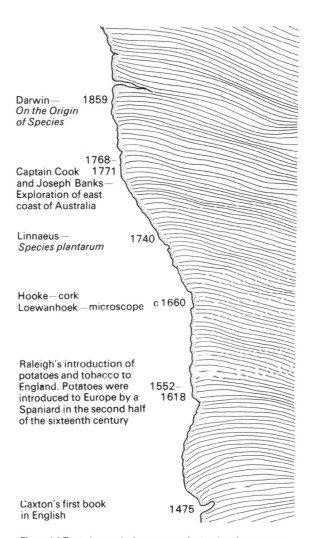

Darwin—
On the Origin of Species　1859

1768–
Captain Cook　1771
and Joseph Banks—
Exploration of east coast of Australia

Linnaeus—
Species plantarum　1740

Hooke—cork
Loewanhoek—microscope　c 1660

Raleigh's introduction of potatoes and tobacco to England. Potatoes were introduced to Europe by a Spaniard in the second half of the sixteenth century　1552–1618

Caxton's first book in English　1475

Figure 1.1 Tree-ring analysis can record a tree's existence over several hundred years

and other *heterotrophic* (mixed-feeding) organisms require. Most plants are anchored in the soil and respond slowly to changes in their environment. You will have noted the careful use of the word 'most'. We can always find plants that break the rules. Some are not green - the copper beech tree has a dark brown pigment that hides the chlorophyll; some are not rooted in the soil - duck-weed floats on water; some have rapid responses to a stimulus - the leaves of *Mimosa pudica* rapidly fold up and collapse when touched (Fig.1.2).

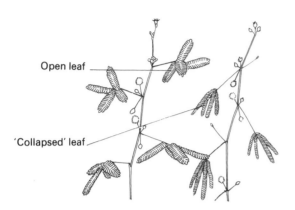

Figure 1.2 The sensitive plant, *Mimosa pudica*

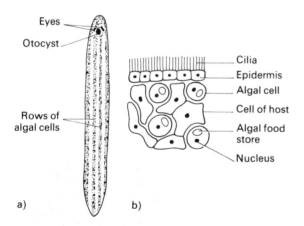

Figure 1.3 *Convoluta roscoffensis* a free-living planarian which relies for its food on the activity of symbiotic algae: a) dorsal view, b) vertical section showing algal cells with chloroplasts

And what is not a plant? When you can confidently recognise plants you may still be confused by some organisms. Although wood anemones are plants, sea anemones are animals! Mushrooms are found on the vegetable counter but belong not to the plant kingdom but to the fungus kingdom and the seaweeds described in all the old botany books are now classified in the kingdom Protoctista.

■ THE ROLE OF PLANTS IN THE BIOSPHERE

Plants and other living things can be found all over the earth from the deepest ocean to the highest mountain; so we call the surface layer of our planet the *biosphere*. Over the whole biosphere plants play an unique role; by their photosynthesis they not only maintain the composition of the air by adding oxygen and removing carbon dioxide, but also produce the food on which all heterotrophic organisms depend. Plants provide other organisms with shade and shelter. Plants also moderate the destructive effects of climate on the environment. They do this by their roots: absorbing water from the soil, holding the soil particles together and protecting it against wind and rain erosion. The carbon cycle (Fig.1.4) shows how the food produced by plants either goes through an animal food chain, being taken up first by herbivores (plant eaters) and then by carnivores (animal eaters), or through a decomposer food chain providing food for bacteria and fungi in the soil. All organisms return inorganic nutrients to the soil and carbon dioxide to the atmosphere to be recycled by the plants.

A simple classification of the plant kingdom is given in Appendix 1 (page 104). Nearly all of the most familiar plants are found in the two groups or phyla; cone-bearing plants (Coniferophyta) and seed-bearing plants (Angiospermophyta). The latter group contains nearly all of the organisms recognised, even by non-biologists, as 'plants'. Angiosperms or flowering plants have true flowers and seeds enclosed in a fruit formed from the ovary. This phylum is divided into two classes, the monocotyledons (or monocots for short) such as lawn grass and wheat, and the dicotyledons (or dicots) such as beans and oak. All of these terms are defined and explained later, but for the moment just think of the *mono*cots as having *one* seed leaf, or *cotyledon* (see Fig.3.17) and narrow grass-like leaves whilst the *di*cots have *two* seed leaves (see Fig.2.1) and broad leaves. In Chapter 2 we will concentrate on the biology of one dicotyledonous plant - the bean.

Angiosperms consist of a root system (generally below ground) and a shoot system above ground level. The roots anchor the plant by spreading through the soil or by forming buttresses at the base of trunks. Roots absorb water and minerals

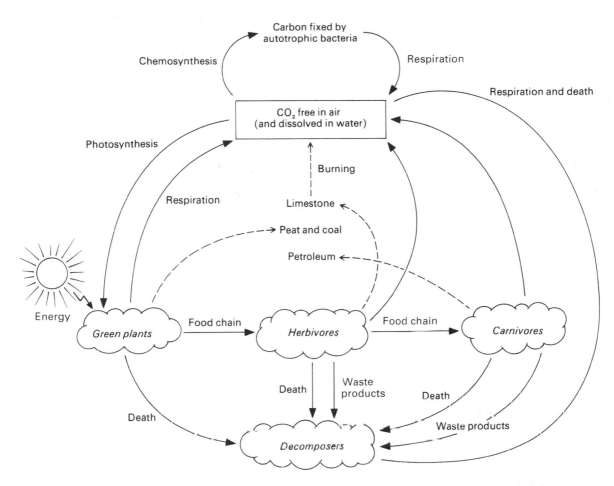

Figure 1.4 The carbon cycle. Pathways shown take minutes to years to accomplish, but those shown by dotted lines lock up the fixed carbon for much longer periods. From each trophic level carbon is returned to the atmosphere as carbon dioxide from respiring tissues. Note: the cycle depends on new inputs of energy from the sun. Energy flows through the food chain, is converted to different forms and eventually to heat energy which is lost to outer space

from the soil and allow drainage channels through the soil so reducing surface run-off of water and soil erosion. Some roots (for example those of mangrove, which lives in waterlogged coastal and riverside habitats) even emerge into the air for gaseous exchange.

The shoot system consists of stems with buds capable of growing into branches, leaves and flowers (Fig.1.5). Stems hold up the green leaves towards the light for photosynthesis and in the best position for gaseous exchange. All of the necessary water and dissolved food materials are carried through the plant in the specialised cells which form the *vascular bundles* (the transport tissues).

Buttress roots

3

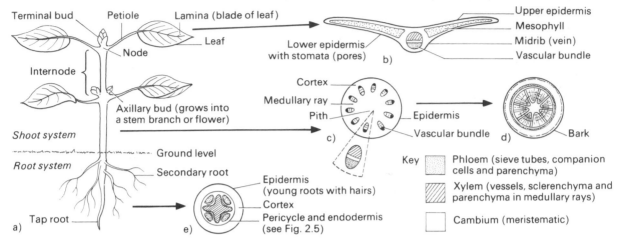

Figure 1.5 a) Structure of a dicotyledonous angiosperm, b) transverse section of a leaf, c) transverse section of a young stem (unthickened), d) transverse section of a woody stem (secondarily thickened), e) transverse section of a young root)

Water is continuously taken up by the root system, passing through the stems and finally lost to the atmosphere through the aerial parts of the plant - a process known as *transpiration* (see Chapter 2).

Leaf mosaic in beech

Leaves have a large surface area and grow to position themselves in a mosaic pattern so that each leaf receives maximum sunlight. You can confirm this by standing under a leafy tree and looking up into the canopy. Leaves have an outer skin, a layer of cells called the *epidermis*, and the bulk of the leaf is made up of *mesophyll* cells. Many mesophyll cells contain chloroplasts, the microscopic structures which contain chlorophyll for photosynthesis. These photosynthetic mesophyll cells form a tissue called the *chlorenchyma*.

Each leaf also has a continuation of the system of vascular bundles for the movement of water and dissolved substances, and a network of air spaces for movement of water vapour and gases.

Parts of flowers are actually modified leaves, and buds can be thought of as telescoped shoots, maintained in a resting condition by the action of a chemical - a plant growth substance called abscisic acid (ABA) - see Chapter 4. A brussel sprout can be identified when cut lengthwise as a large bud with stem, leaves and smaller buds (Fig.1.6).

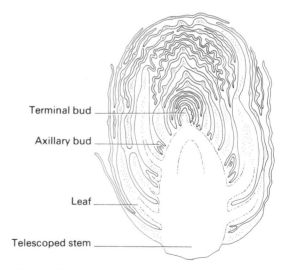

Figure 1.6 Vertical section of a brussel sprout (a giant bud)

Up to this point you will have read about some basic facts concerning the structure of flowering plants (the study of *morphology*). We should now consider the microscopical study of cells (*cytology*) and groups of similar cells or tissues (*histology*). You may have made your own microscope preparations by cutting very thin slices of plant material and mounting the sections on glass slides. More permanent preparations can be made by dehydrating the tissues with alcohol and staining them with different dyes to show different tissue types (see Appendix 2 on stains page 105). Fig.1.7 shows a range of different plant cells as they appear when using a light microscope. The obvious features are the nuclei (containing chromosomes), the cytoplasm and the cell wall. Plant cell walls are made of the carbohydrate *cellulose*.

(Note: animal cells do not have either cellulose or cell walls.)

The cells of root systems are formed at the root tips by a process of cell division called *mitosis*, and these regions of cell division are known as *meristems*. There are also meristems in shoot tips and, in addition, new cells are produced in leaf bases, in special tissues (called *cambium*) of the vascular bundles and under the bark of stems. The newly produced cells are said to be undifferentiated, small and packed tightly together. As they grow and change (i.e. *differentiate*) they become specialised to perform particular functions. Some differentiated cells have in their cell walls, lignin (wood) and others have suberin (cork). Details of a few basic cell types are given in Table 1.1 and illustrated in Fig.1.7.

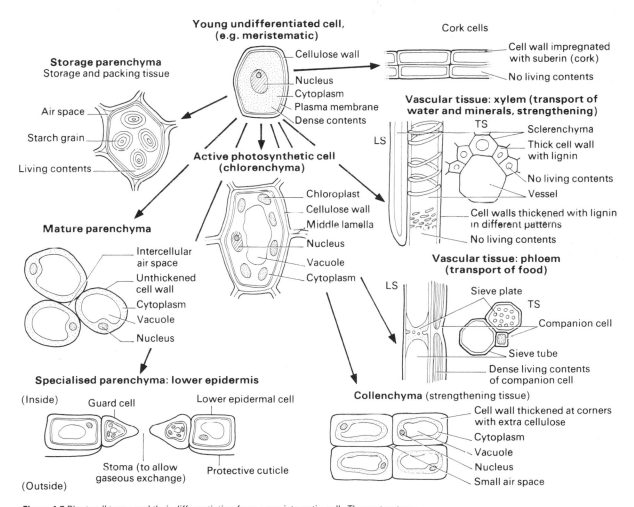

Figure 1.7 Plant cell types and their differentiation from a meristematic cell. These structures can be seen using a light microscope

5

Tissue type	Where found	Function
Parenchyma	In young tissues (meristems) mesophyll of leaves and as 'packing tissue' in roots and stems, e.g. cortex and pith (Fig.1.5)	• In meristems – are capable of division • In cortex and pith – support plant because of water absorption and turgidity • Store foods
Chlorenchyma	In leaves – they contain chloroplasts	Photosynthesis
Collenchyma	Under epidermis of stem	Cells thickened with cellulose strips so give extra support to non-woody stems
Sclerenchyma	In vascular bundles	Strengthening tissues Tightly packed, thickened with lignin (wood) to support stems
Vessels	Xylem in vascular bundles	Elongated cells joined end to end to form water-conducting tubes
Sieve tubes	Phloem in vascular bundles	Unthickened elongated cells joined end to end by sieve plates to form tubes which transport foods and other cell products. Cells with living contents

Table 1.1

The illustrations (Figs.1.8, 1.9, 1.10 and 1.11) show microscope preparations of transverse sections of a stem, root and leaf. Examine them carefully and try to identify the different tissues listed in Table 1.1.

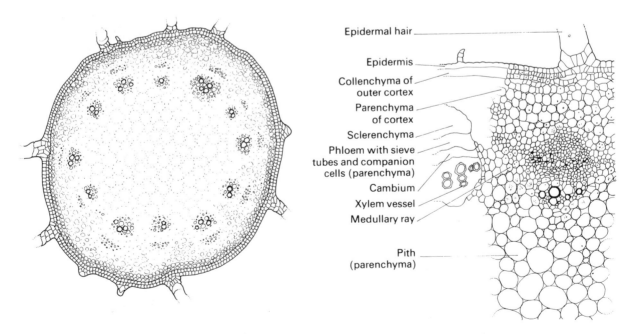

Figure 1.8 Transverse section of a sunflower (*Helianthus* sp.) stem, dicotyledon

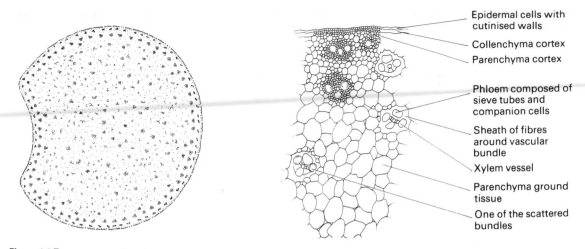

Epidermal cells with
cutinised walls

Collenchyma cortex

Parenchyma cortex

Phloem composed of
sieve tubes and
companion cells

Sheath of fibres
around vascular
bundle

Xylem vessel

Parenchyma ground
tissue

One of the scattered
bundles

Figure 1.9 Transverse section of a maize (*Zea* sp.) stem, monocotyledon

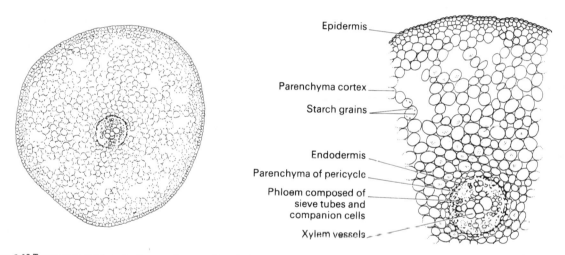

Epidermis

Parenchyma cortex

Starch grains

Endodermis

Parenchyma of pericycle

Phloem composed of
sieve tubes and
companion cells

Xylem vessels

Figure 1.10 Transverse section of a *Ranunculus* root, dicotyledon

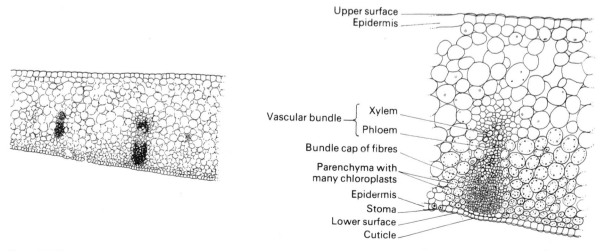

Upper surface
Epidermis

Vascular bundle — Xylem

Phloem

Bundle cap of fibres

Parenchyma with
many chloroplasts

Epidermis

Stoma

Lower surface

Cuticle

Figure 1.11 Transverse section of the mesophyte leaf of Iris - monocotyledon. Compare this with the transverse section of a broad bean (*Vicia faba*) - dicotyledon. See Fig.2.15 on page 25

■ THE ANGIOSPERM LIFE CYCLE

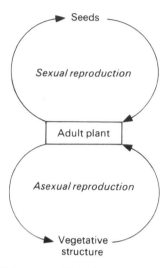

Figure 1.12 Angiosperm life cycle

Woody trees and shrubs may take many years to mature to the state where they can produce flowers and seeds. Herbaceous (non-woody) *annuals* and *biennials* have life cycles lasting one and two years respectively. Examples are the annual groundsel (Fig.1.13) and the biennial wild carrot (Fig.6.5). Other herbaceous plants (*perennials*) survive longer by having perennating organs in which food is stored for new growth the following year.

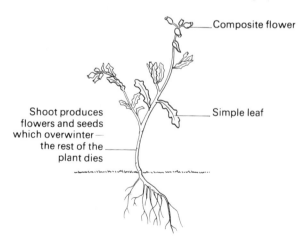

Figure 1.13 Groundsel (*Senecio vulgaris*), an annual with overwintering seeds

---

germination the development of a seed into a seedling or young plant

vegetative growth the development of plants from some structure other than a seed

---

Some examples are the onion bulb and potato stem tuber (see Chapter 6), celandine root tuber (see Fig.1.14) and couch grass rhizome. These plants develop further as **vegetative growth** from the perennating organs but may also produce seeds which **germinate** and grow into new plants (see Chapter 3). We have exploited many perennating organs for food.

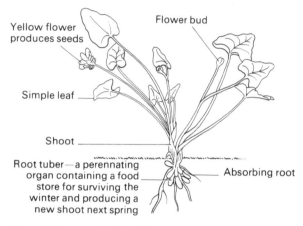

Figure 1.14 Lesser celandine (*Ranunculus ficaria*), a perennial

■ Seed dispersal

Seeds are embryo plants packaged with a stored food supply. Thus they are excellent overwintering devices, maintaining a species through unfavourable times until conditions become suitable for germination. But first they must be dispersed - or spread away from the parent plant - to avoid too much competition for space.

Seeds can remain **viable** and capable of germination for many years; some causing the blooming of deserts after years of drought. Others that require light, like the common poppy, will suddenly germinate only when waste ground is disturbed. However, very old seeds often show abnormalities, resulting in loss of viability, perhaps

---

viable seeds of the lotus plant (*Nelumbium nucifera*) are the oldest known viable seeds and were found in a drained lake bed in Manchuria in 1926. Radioactive carbon dating showed them to be about 1050 years old! In 1951 treatment by sulphuric acid to break down the seed coats produced nearly 100% germination

---

owing to slow chemical changes such as the denaturing of proteins. Seeds unearthed by archaeologists are used to tell us about the food of early humans.

Dispersal is necessary to prevent overcrowding and the resulting competition for light and nutrients between the seedlings and the parent plant, although there is enormous wastage in seeds that do not reach the correct environmental conditions for survival. The advantage of seed dispersal is the colonisation of neighbouring land, increasing the overall size of the population. Seeds are dispersed either within the whole *fruit* or singly after the rupture of the fruit (Examples can be seen in Fig.1.15). It is the development of the ovary wall

following fertilisation which determines the nature of the fruit and how it is dispersed (see Chapter 3).

The agents for dispersal are animals, wind and water currents, and by self-propulsion or explosive mechanisms.

Succulent and nutty fruits are eaten by birds, bats, mice and other mammals which carry them away from the parent plant. Seeds that pass undamaged through the bodies of animals, e.g. bramble, are deposited with the faeces and have the advantage of being dispersed with their own fertiliser supply! Animals also disperse sticky or hooked seeds and fruits on their fur or feathers. You may have had difficulty in removing the burdock burrs from your clothing because of the hooked bracts enclosing the fruits. In succulent fruits, such as plums and

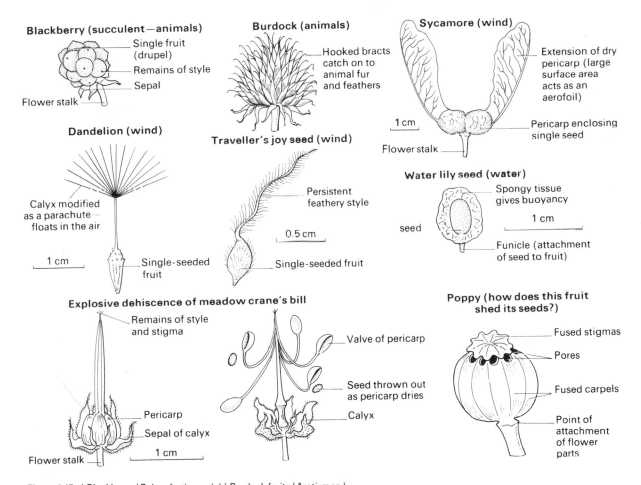

Figure 1.15 a) Blackberry (*Rubus fruticosus*), b) Burdock fruits (*Arctium* sp.),
c) Sycamore fruits (*Acer pseudoplatanus*), d) Dandelion fruit (*Taraxacum officinale*),
e) Traveller's-joy fruit (*Clematis vitalba*), f) Water lily seed (*Nuphar lutea*), g) Meadow crane's-bill fruits (*Geranium pratense*), h) Poppy fruit (*Papaver* sp.)

tomatoes, the ovary wall differentiates into a layered *pericarp*; with the skin enclosing a mass of succulent parenchyma and often a central stony layer enclosing the seed(s). Other juicy fruits, such as apples and strawberries are termed *false fruits* as the succulent structure derives from the receptacle (top of the flower stalk), and the fruit is the pip (Fig.1.16).

a)

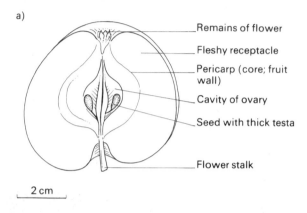

- Remains of flower
- Fleshy receptacle
- Pericarp (core; fruit wall)
- Cavity of ovary
- Seed with thick testa
- Flower stalk

2 cm

b)

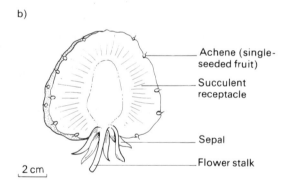

- Achene (single-seeded fruit)
- Succulent receptacle
- Sepal
- Flower stalk

2 cm

Figure 1.16 False fruits of a) apple (*Malus* sp.) and b) strawberry (*Fragaria* sp.)

Q 1. Many tomato plants are found growing on sewage farms. Why?

2. In your field study, observe and draw specimens of plants with different methods of dispersal.

Some fruits and seeds have extensions to their dry pericarp to act as aerofoils, e.g. sycamore and birch, or parts of the carpel form feathery structures, e.g. the pappus of hairs (calyx) of the dandelion or style of traveller's-joy.

Water-carried fruits contain buoyant tissue so that they float, e.g. the coconut, which has a thick fibrous coat around the woody shell, and the water-lily.

The explosive mechanisms shown by many plants of the Leguminoseae and Crucifereae families (Appendix 1) are caused by unequal drying and changes in the turgidity of the pericarp. Self-propulsion (explosion or dehiscence) is probably the most dramatic method of dispersal. If you sit quietly in the warm sun on a gorse-covered hillside you may hear the pods popping open as the valves twist and shoot out the seeds.

■ **Asexual reproduction**

Vegetative propagation or ***asexual reproduction*** occurs when a relatively large part of the plant forms an independent shoot. Examples are the nettle, where the underground stem branches in all directions forming clumps of nettles, and the spreading plants of wild strawberry with their runners (branch stems) running on the surface of the ground (Fig.1.17). Many such asexual structures are also perennating organs (see Chapter 6).

Asexual reproduction has the advantage that a plant can continue to exploit a favourable habitat. There are, on the other hand, disadvantages in asexual reproduction, the most important being the inevitable overcrowding and competition, and the lack of new genetic variation that is achieved with sexual reproduction.

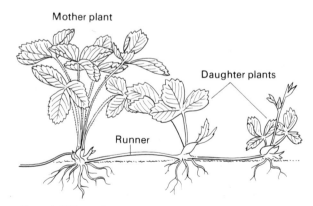

Mother plant

Daughter plants

Runner

Figure 1.17 Vegetative propagation: strawberry runner

asexual reproduction the production of daughter plants with identical genes to the single parent. The daughter plants are formed from vegetative parts of the plant instead of from seeds

PLANTS AND WATER

Life on earth started in the oceans and by a very slow evolutionary process the land was eventually colonised, first with plants, later with animals. Land is a much harsher environment than water. Temperature fluctuations are greater, organisms are exposed to the sun, wind and rain, and the weight of the body has to be supported without the buoyancy of water. Special problems occur with sexual reproduction, such as how one gamete (sex cell) reaches the other without a water medium (see Chapter 3). Some plant groups, e.g. ferns, have sperm which swim from the male sex organs through water on the plant surface to the female egg cell to fertilise it.

Q Compare the problems of life on land for animals with those of plants: do you think they are the same? If not, why not?

The biggest problem of all for any terrestrial plant is the conservation of water, essential for metabolism and support.

Water evaporates mainly from holes in the plant, i.e. *stomata* in the leaves (Fig.2.13) and *lenticels* in the stem (Fig.1.21 and Chapter 2). Structures which are thin enough to allow rapid **diffusion** of gases for respiration and photosynthesis are also vulnerable to *desiccation* (drying up). Plants have to make a compromise between the necessity of having openings to let gases in and out and the need to make them small enough to prevent dehydration by evaporation. How do they manage to cope with this problem in extreme conditions?

> **diffusion** the movement of a substance from a region of high concentration of that substance to a region of low concentration

INVESTIGATION

WHAT DIFFERENCE DOES HAVING STOMATA MAKE TO REDUCING WATER LOSS?

The figures in Table 1.2 were obtained by using petri dishes that were either uncovered, (**1**), or covered with a zinc mesh of different sizes, (**2**) and (**3**).

Q 1. Work out the percentage of the 400 mm^2 surface area that is exposed (x_1 and x_2).

2. Work out the percentage of the water loss (y_1 and y_2).

3. Place the three dishes in order of water loss.

4. List the dishes in order of water evaporated per unit area exposed.

5. What does this tell us about pore size and water loss from plants?

6. Carry out an investigation to compare the distribution of stomata in a grass leaf from a) a wood and b) an open field, by examining leaf samples under a microscope with top illumination and counting the number of stomata in the field of view.

	Area (mm^2)	Nature of surface	Area exposed		Amount of water lost in 15 h at 25°C	
			(mm^2)	(%)	(g)	(%)
1	400	Open	400	100	2.46	100
2	400	196 pores	18.2	x_1	0.92	y_1
3	400	49 pores	4.55	x_2	0.27	y_2

Table 1.2

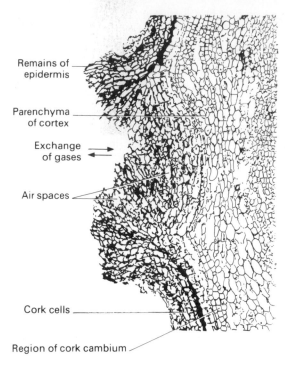

Remains of epidermis

Parenchyma of cortex

Exchange of gases

Air spaces

Cork cells

Region of cork cambium

Figure 1.18 Vertical section of a lenticel of elder (*Sambucus*)

Figure 1.19 Glasswort (*Salicornia* sp.). Note its succulent stem and reduced leaves in which high levels of salt are stored. Why?

■ Dry habitats

Plants living in dry habitats with limited or spasmodic water supply, such as deserts, are known as *xerophytes*. Features which tend to reduce water loss from a plant are therefore known as *xeromorphic* characters.

There are several ways in which plants control their water balance. Plants most efficient in water conservation will use a combination of methods. One is by storing it in large quantities when it is available, during monsoon rains for example. (A baobab tree was found to hold nearly 100 000 litres of water in its trunk and travellers in the desert know that if they cut into the stem of a cactus, water will drip out!) Plants with thick and fleshy parts are called *succulents*. In Europe, succulents such as stonecrop can be found on garden walls, open hillsides or dunes where rain soon drains away, and another, glasswort (Fig.1.19) lives on salt marshes where fresh water is scarce.

Another method is to collect water efficiently. Some desert plants have shallow roots spreading over a wide area to pick up dew. Tamarisk, however, has roots which may penetrate as much as 50 m down to tap the water table. Some sand dune plants have similar adaptations for survival (Fig.1.20).

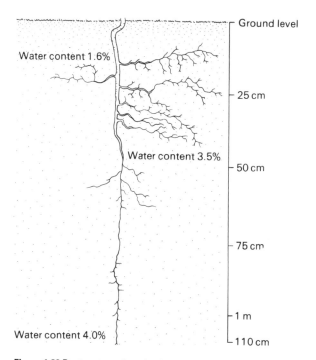

Ground level

Water content 1.6%

25 cm

Water content 3.5%

50 cm

75 cm

1 m

Water content 4.0%

110 cm

Figure 1.20 Root system of portland spurge (*Euphorbia portlandica*) from a partially fixed dune, and the percentage water content of soil

Modifications of the plant body can also limit or slow down the loss of water. Leaf surface area may be reduced to an extreme, as in cacti (which may have only a tenth the surface area of a similar-sized deciduous plant) with its leaves reduced to spines and with the succulent green stem taking over as the main photosynthetic organ. Gorse is a common British example where both stem and leaf spines are found. The leaves of evergreen conifers are narrow needles, reducing the surface area available for water loss. Evaporation may be reduced by having stomata opening into humid cavities, e.g. the rolled leaves of marram (Fig.1.21), or the sunken stomata of privet.

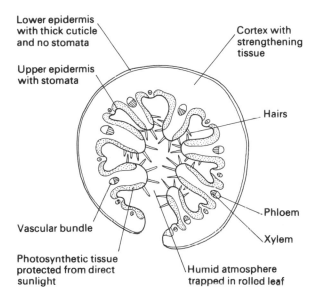

Lower epidermis with thick cuticle and no stomata

Upper epidermis with stomata

Cortex with strengthening tissue

Hairs

Vascular bundle

Phloem

Xylem

Photosynthetic tissue protected from direct sunlight

Humid atmosphere trapped in rolled leaf

Figure 1.21 Transverse section of a leaf of marram (*Ammophila arenaria*) to show xeromorphic characters (low power plan drawn from a microscope slide)

Sand sedge

Q 1. Devise methods for a) comparing the rate of transpiration in different species and b) comparing humidity at different heights above the ground in a wood.

2. Describe xeromorphic characters in dune plants.

The direct evaporation of water from the leaf epidermis can be reduced by various modifications. Wax, a water-repellent fatty compound, forms a shiny, varnish-like layer (usually mainly on the upper epidermis exposed to sunlight). This not only reduces excessive water loss but also protects against penetration by potential parasites and from mechanical injury. An example is the thick waxy cuticle of holly. Hairs on the leaf (e.g. great mullein) also reduce transpiration by enclosing the leaf in humid air. With hairy and waxy surfaces, and down-pointing spines, rain quickly runs off the surface to the ground where it is immediately available to the roots. These modifications incidentally hamper the hungry advances of small herbivores!

Another habitat where water may be scarce is up in the air! Many ground-living high-altitude plants are hairy (e.g. mountain avens). Others live as *epiphytes* (plants that grow on the surface of another plant) above the ground, in the forks of trees or in crevices in the bark. They carry out their own photosynthesis so are totally independent in their nutritional requirements. The host trees simply provide a foothold where there is plenty of light, but rain, carrying nutrients, can reach them. Roots often just hang down in the humid air - this is certainly true of tropical rainforest epiphytes.

'Air-plants' have become popular as house plants. What adaptations do you think they have to enable them to survive in British homes?

The stems (trunks) of trees and shrubs develop a waterproof layer of cork, reducing evaporation. Cork is found in abundance in the cork oak, grown in Spain and the south of France as a crop plant. Cork forms only a thin layer in most British trees and is produced by a layer of meristematic cells called the cork cambium (*phellogen*) which usually arises under the epidermis (Fig.1.22). The first ever drawing of plant cells was published by Robert Hooke in 1665 in his famous *Micrographia*.

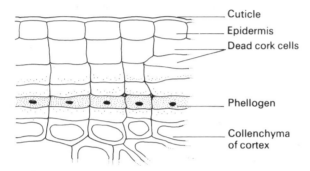

Figure 1.22 Cork formation in potato, vertical section of outer cortex

The phellogen divides to form cells in which *suberin*, the corky material, is deposited in association with the layers of cellulose. Suberin is a complex, highly-polymerised compound of fatty acids. It is *hydrophobic* (i.e. it repels water). With decreasing day length and temperature, the tissues produce plant growth substances, in particular *ethene*. Apart from being concerned in the breakdown of pigments, production of autumn colour and the ripening of fruit, ethene also brings about leaf fall. First, an *abscission* layer forms at the base of stalks of deciduous leaves or fruits (Fig.1.23) and then suberin is deposited in a cork layer. This eventually seals the vascular bundles, preventing movement in and out of the veins of the leaf and stopping infection by disease organisms after leaf fall. With no leaves, water loss from the tree is greatly reduced in winter. Low temperatures freeze soil water, making it unavailable to the roots by normal uptake. This is known as *physiological drought*.

> **Robert Hooke** (1635-1703) was the first person to use the word 'cell' and was renowned for his meticulous observation. "I ... found that there were usually about three score of these small cells placed end-ways in the eighteenth part of an inch in length ..."

Another advantage of leaf fall is that it allows the plant to get rid of metabolic waste substances that have been accumulated and stored in the leaf, a part of plant excretion.

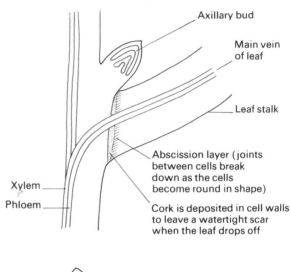

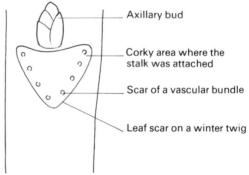

Figure 1.23 How a leaf falls, e.g. sycamore (*Acer pseudoplatanus*)

■ Water-abundant habitats

Where water is abundant, in streams and rivers, leaves are relatively thinner and softer than in terrestrial plants. They can absorb water and dissolved gases through the exposed stomata in the leaf surface. Water plants, known as *hydrophytes*, have little strengthening tissue; when you lift them up they flop limply. The leaves and stems contain many air spaces between the cells, giving them buoyancy and keeping the leaves near the water surface to receive sufficient light (Fig.1.24). Aerial and submerged leaves on the same plant may be morphologically (structurally) different.

Rainforest trees grow luxuriantly in high rainfall. Water is quickly taken up by the tree roots and their

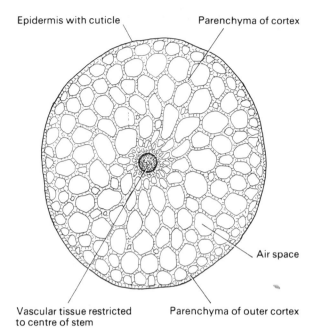

Epidermis with cuticle   Parenchyma of cortex

Air space

Vascular tissue restricted   Parenchyma of outer cortex
to centre of stem

Figure 1.24 Transverse section of the stem of mare's tail. Why can this stem not support itself out of water?

symbiotic fungi (*mycorrhiza*) which have a very large surface area for absorption. This, together with the rapid decomposition of plant remains on the forest floor, means that the soil in such a forest is impoverished. It is of little use in growing crops once the trees have been cleared, indicating the futility of tropical deforestation for agriculture. In addition, once large areas of trees are cut down, wind and sun reach the ground and dry it up, creating unsuitable conditions for seedlings to develop and crops die. This contrasts with the natural conditions when the death of individual trees opens up small glades enabling young saplings to regenerate the forest. Within the forest, wind speed is reduced, the canopy prevents most of the sunlight reaching the ground, and high humidity at ground level results. The closely-growing, luxuriant plants compete for light. There are many climbers that reach the canopy on the backs of tall trees. Epiphytes are particularly common high off the ground.

> **symbiosis** a close, dependent and long-lasting relationship between two or more species, for example algae in coral cells, and the algae and fungus forming a lichen

◼ GROWTH

Growth is defined as an increase in dry mass. It does not take place uniformly over the whole plant but only where cell division occurs in growing regions called *meristems* - groups of actively-dividing undifferentiated cells. These are divided into *primary meristems* (present in the embryo) at the tips of shoots and roots (Fig.1.25), and *secondary meristems* which develop later, e.g. the stem cambium, which permits increase in girth (*secondary thickening*) to form wood (Fig.1.26).

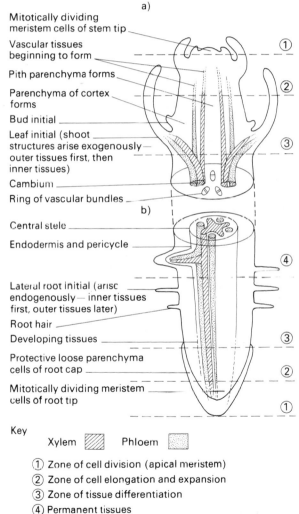

a)

Mitotically dividing meristem cells of stem tip

Vascular tissues beginning to form ①

Pith parenchyma forms ②

Parenchyma of cortex forms

Bud initial

Leaf initial (shoot structures arise exogenously— outer tissues first, then inner tissues) ③

Cambium

Ring of vascular bundles

b)

Central stele

Endodermis and pericycle ④

Lateral root initial (arise endogenously— inner tissues first, outer tissues later)

Root hair

Developing tissues ③

Protective loose parenchyma cells of root cap ②

Mitotically dividing meristem cells of root tip ①

Key

Xylem ▨   Phloem ▦

① Zone of cell division (apical meristem)
② Zone of cell elongation and expansion
③ Zone of tissue differentiation
④ Permanent tissues

Figure 1.25 Transverse section of: a) a shoot apex and b) a root apex

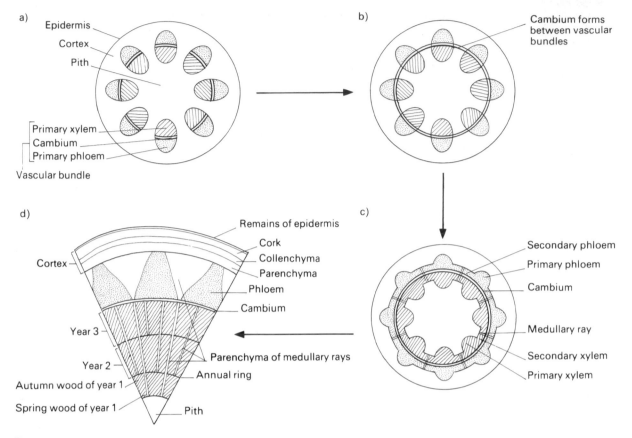

Figure 1.26 Transverse section showing the stages in secondary thickening in a dicotyledonous stem: a) the young stem, b) development of cambium between the vascular bundles, c) secondary phloem and xylem produced by division of the cambium between the bundles, d) a three year old stem showing annual rings

Once cells differentiate and become specialised, they are no longer capable of division, indeed some, for example xylem vessels, lose their living contents entirely (Fig.1.7). Development is controlled by *plant growth substances*, but is dependent on a supply of water and nutrients and a suitable temperature. Plant growth substances, such as *cytokinins*, control cell division, while others, *gibberellins* and *auxins*, control the elongation of cells and their differentiation.

The counting of annual rings is the basis of the science of *dendrochronology*. A tree lays down a new ring of wood (xylem) each year. The cells produced in this layer are larger in spring than in late summer. The result is a series of concentric rings and we can count the years (Fig.1.1). The width of an annual ring reflects the growth of the tree, bad growing years being recognised as narrow rings. By matching the pattern of rings and counting back, dates can be established. Dendrochronologists have gone back to 5150 BC by examining dead bristlecone pines.

■ SENESCENCE

Eventually, as with all living organisms, metabolism slows down and death occurs. Tree leaves have a short life span. *Deciduous* trees (e.g. oak) lose their leaves in winter. *Evergreen* trees (such as pine) lose some leaves throughout the year, never all at once. There is a direct correlation between metabolic rate and longevity. Plants have a low metabolic rate and some trees can live for many hundreds of years. Mature oaks in Britain may be 300 years old, but these are mere children compared with the oldest in the world, the bristlecone pine, reputed to be 4920 years old with a possible life span of 5000-6000 years.

BROAD BEANS, FRENCH BEANS AND HEINZ BEANZ!

Different beans

Healthy broad bean plants

Why the broad bean? Well, apart from the fact that one of the authors has spent many years researching this fascinating plant, the broad bean (*Vicia faba*) is grown widely as a human and animal foodstuff; so the plant is important and has been much studied (in fact, you may well have germinated bean seeds in your own earlier studies in science). The seeds are readily available and can be easily germinated indoors. They are bigger than most seeds and, after soaking in water overnight, can easily be dissected to reveal structures only visible in other seeds with the aid of a microscope. Hence it may be a very suitable species for you to use as a subject for investigative studies. Certainly the material in this chapter will provide you with the basic information about angiosperms in general. The structure

(*morphology*) and functions (*physiology*) of this one species can be taken as typical of annual dicotyledonous angiosperms.

When you buy broad beans from the greengrocer the pods have to be opened to reveal the row of seeds. In the normal course of events the pods and their seeds remain on the plants and dry so that the seeds drop to the ground, where some will eventually germinate and others will be dispersed further away from the parent plant by animals. An individual seed consists of the stored food supply in the *cotyledons*, and the miniature embryo plant with root and shoot (Fig.2.1a). The whole is enclosed in a *testa* - the tough protective seed coat. When the seed matures after a period of *dormancy germination* starts. This is a series of changes controlled by *plant growth substances* (chemicals produced by the plant to control the cell processes). The actions of some of these substances (gibberellins, cytokinins, auxins and phytochrome) are discussed later. The broad bean is typical of the group of plants that germinate with the cotyledons below the soil (*hypogeal* - Fig.2.1c) but the closely related species, the French bean, belongs to the other group of plants where the cotyledons are carried above ground level during germination (*epigeal* - Fig.2.1b).

Germination of a seed follows several distinct stages:

• *Imbibition* (intake) of water which swells the seed, splitting the testa.
• Absorbed water dissolves and activates the seed enzymes which convert insoluble food stores into a soluble form that can be taken to the *embryo* where it is needed for growth and energy.
• The developing root (*radicle*) emerges and starts to function.
• The developing shoot (*plumule*) emerges from the testa and grows.
• Once above soil level the shoot straightens (unhooks) in response to light, a process known as *photomorphogenesis* (see page 53).

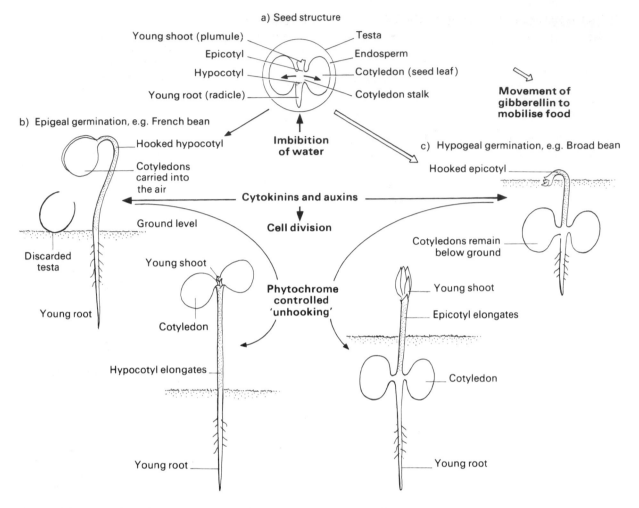

Figure 2.1 Diagrams to show: a) the structure of a seed and the differences between b) epigeal and c) hypogeal germination in dicotyledons. The diagrams also show the plant growth substances controlling germination

Look at Fig.2.1 and work out suitable answers to these questions:

 1. Why is it important to the plant that the root develops first?

2. What is the function of the root hairs, and later, the lateral roots?

3. Why does the shoot emerge hooked?

4. Is there any advantage in epigeal as opposed to hypogeal germination?

The apparently simple method of growing beans on damp blotting paper in a jam jar can be developed as an experimental tool to give data about seeds and their growth.

■ DESIGNING AN EXPERIMENT

• Decide on what you want to test and state this as your hypothesis.
• Devise a method that will test the hypothesis.
• Decide how to record your results and observations.
• Now carry out the experiment and collect results (data).
• Assess your results in the light of your hypothesis and come to some conclusion about it. If your results are inconclusive, devise further methods to test a modified hypothesis.

■ THE RAW MATERIALS FOR GROWTH IN THE ADULT PLANT

Like all plants, the broad bean requires water, carbon in the form of carbon dioxide, and mineral salts, from its environment. In order to grow the plant makes or *synthesises* complex carbon compounds, a process known as *carbon assimilation.* This is described in detail in *Biology Advanced Studies - Biochemistry.* Some of these compounds make the tissues of the plant body, others being used in respiration to provide the energy for the synthesis. Let us consider how the bean plant gets all these raw materials and uses them.

■ Water

Water is present around soil particles, and roots respond by growing towards the stimulus of moisture. *Root hairs* are extensions of epidermal cells and are found just behind the growing tips of the roots (Fig.2.2), greatly increasing the surface area for the absorption of water by the process of *osmosis.* Osmosis is the *diffusion* of water from the soil through a *partially permeable membrane,* (the cell surface membrane) into the cell. This takes place because the soil water has a *water potential* (given the Greek letter psi ψ) which is higher (a less negative value) than the solution in the cell, which has a lower (or more negative) water potential (Fig.2.3).

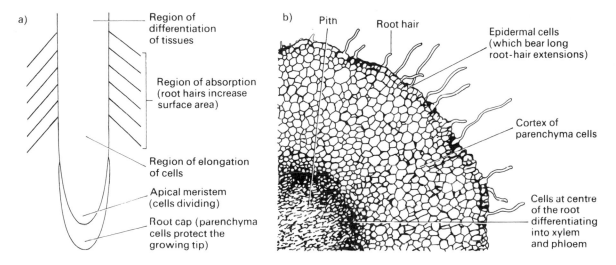

Figure 2.2 Transverse section of *Vicia faba:* a) root tip and b) a root in the region of the root hairs

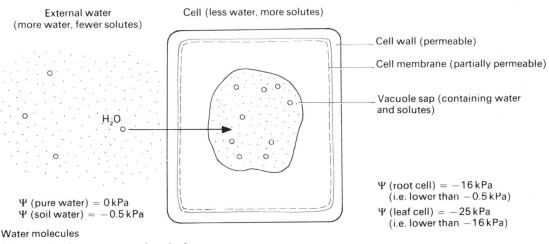

Figure 2.3 Water movement from the soil. Note: water moves from a region of higher potential to a region of lower potential.

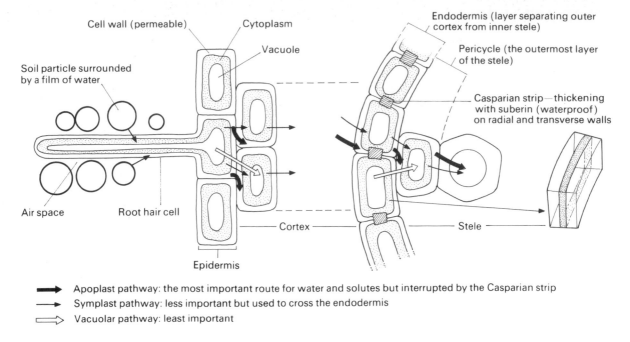

Cell wall (permeable) Cytoplasm

Vacuole

Soil particle surrounded by a film of water

Endodermis (layer separating outer cortex from inner stele)

Pericycle (the outermost layer of the stele)

Casparian strip—thickening with suberin (waterproof) on radial and transverse walls

Air space   Root hair cell

Cortex

Stele

Epidermis

➡ Apoplast pathway: the most important route for water and solutes but interrupted by the Casparian strip
→ Symplast pathway: less important but used to cross the endodermis
⇨ Vacuolar pathway: least important

Figure 2.4 Root hair cell in relation to soil particles, and the movement of water and solutes into the xylem through the endodermis and pericycle

The soil water is a very dilute *solution* of minerals compared with the sap inside the root hair which contains more **solutes**, in other words, less water. Between the two is the permeable *cellulose* wall, through which many substances can pass freely. Inside the wall is the cell surface membrane which is partially permeable and through which only small molecules, such as water, can pass (Fig.2.4).

The water potential (ψ) of pure water, measured in kilopascals (kPa), is zero. When solutes are present the value for ψ is negative. The pressure or strength of a solution is called the *solute potential* (ψ_s). The more solutes present (in terms of numbers of molecules for a unit volume), the more negative the value for ψ.

When a cell is full of water it is *turgid* and capable of supporting the cell and maintaining its shape. The push inwards of the stretched walls of the cell exerts a pressure on the contents of the cell known as the *pressure potential* (ψ_p). This has positive value in a turgid cell, limiting how much water can be taken into a cell by osmosis.

solutes the substances dissolved in a solvent to produce a solution

We can link these terms as follows:
Water potential (ψ) = solute potential (ψ_s) + pressure potential (ψ_p).

Q Look at the values for ψ given in Fig.2.5 and see if you can decide which way water is going to move. (The answer is on page 38.)

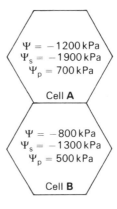

$\Psi = -1200\,kPa$
$\Psi_s = -1900\,kPa$
$\Psi_p = 700\,kPa$

Cell **A**

$\Psi = -800\,kPa$
$\Psi_s = -1300\,kPa$
$\Psi_p = 500\,kPa$

Cell **B**

Figure 2.5 Water potential: In which direction will water move between these two living cells?

■ TO DETERMINE THE SOLUTE POTENTIAL OF CELLS

If cells are placed in a strong salt or sugar solution, water is drawn out of the cells, causing the protoplast to shrink away from the cell wall. The cells are then said to be *plasmolysed*. The shrinkage can be used to determine experimentally the solute potential of the cells in a tissue (e.g. epidermis) by placing the tissue in a range of solutions of different known molarity and examining them under a microscope (Fig.2.6).

1. Make up a series of salt solutions starting with 2M (11.7 g NaCl dissolved in water and the total volume made up to 100 cm³). Take 50 cm³ of this solution and add 50 cm³ of water. Label this as a 1M (molar) solution. Make sure the solution is well mixed, then remove 10 cm³ and make it up to 100 cm³ with water to give a 0.1M solution and label it.

Make up 0.01M and 0.001M solutions by dilution in a similar way and label them. This process is known as *serial dilution*.

2. Tear strips of epidermis from broad bean leaves. Add one to each of the solutions and leave for 15 minutes. (Why?)

3. Place each strip in turn on a microscope slide. Where water has been lost from the vacuole the cell membrane is pulled away from the cell wall. Cells where the gap can be seen (plasmolysed cells) are counted and the percentage of plasmolysed cells calculated and plotted against the molarity of the solution. *Incipient plasmolysis* is where 50% of the cells display some shrinkage of the cytoplasm. The molarity where this occurs is taken as the solute potential of the cells (Fig.2.7). Note: if broad bean leaves are not available use the epidermis of the inner scales of an onion.

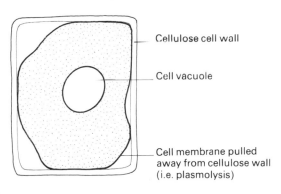

Cellulose cell wall

Cell vacuole

Cell membrane pulled away from cellulose wall (i.e. plasmolysis)

Figure 2.6

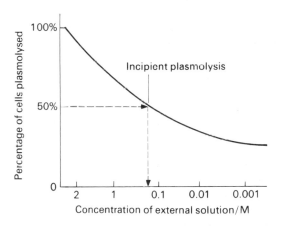

Figure 2.7 Graph illustrating incipient plasmolysis

Because there is a difference in water potential between the soil water and the root hair cell, water diffuses into the cell. This makes the water potential of this cell less negative than neighbouring cells in the root cortex and so water passes into these cells. As a result, a gradient of water potential is set up between the epidermis and the central transport area (*stele*) of the root (Fig.2.4).

There are two routes by which water passes from cell to cell across the cortex. The a*poplastic pathway* (*apoplasm*), where the water passes through or between the cellulose walls without going through the cytoplasm itself, and the *symplastic pathway* (*symplasm*). Here the water passes through the living cytoplasm from cell to cell, including moving through *plasmodesmata* (fine threads of cytoplasm linking one cell to a neighbouring cell through tiny holes in the cellulose cell walls) (Fig.2.4).

Cells of the *endodermis*, the innermost layer of cells in the cortex, regulate water flow. The cells have a band of thickening around their tangential walls called the *casparian strip*. The casparian strip is waterproof so water cannot pass through these cells by apoplasm but only by symplasm. Water then passes through the *pericycle* lining the endodermis until it reaches vessels of the xylem.

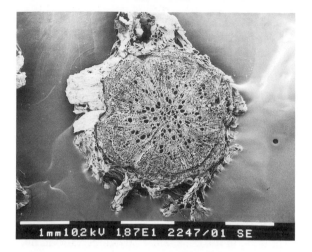

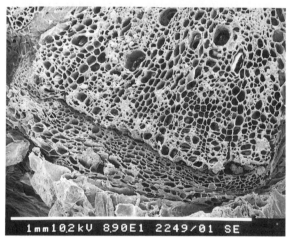

Electron micrographs of transverse section of *Vicia faba* root at increasing magnification, x 12 (above) and x 56 (below)

Each xylem vessel is a continuous thick-walled tube running from one end of the plant to the other, and, unlike other cells, has no living contents so that water cannot get into it by osmosis. Instead, water enters and moves upwards by other processes. *Root pressure* from water entering the roots pushes water from below and **transpiration** exerts a pull from above.

---

transpiration the loss of water from the above ground parts of a plant. Transpiration occurs through the small pores, the stomata, mainly on the underside of the leaves, and through the small holes, the lenticels, on the stem

---

We can start with a familiar experience. Wet clothes on the line dry quickest when it is warm and windy and when the air is dry with low humidity. This is because *evaporation* (the change of water from liquid to vapour) requires heat. If the vapour is then carried away from the clothes, a gradient of humidity is set up and more water can be evaporated from the clothes. The same factors affect the rate at which water transpires from leaves. The cells in the leaf generate heat during their chemical activities and so water moves from inside the cell to the cell's outer surface and then into intercellular air spaces, taking heat from the plant. The vapour then diffuses out into the air through the stomata.

Transpiration draws up more water through the xylem owing to the physical properties of water molecules. The xylem vessels have a very small diameter (up to about 0.2 mm) and act as capillary tubes. The water molecules stick to the wall of the tube (*adhesion*) and creep up the sides of the tubes (*capillarity*). In addition, the chains of water molecules in the vessels stick together (*cohesion*). So, pulling from the top (like when using a drinking straw) draws water up the tube (Fig.2.8). These processes work equally well in a relatively short bean plant and the tallest trees, where water must get to the highest leaves. The patterns of thickening in the walls of the vessels (Fig.1.26) are necessary to stop the vessels collapsing under the suction effect of transpiration.

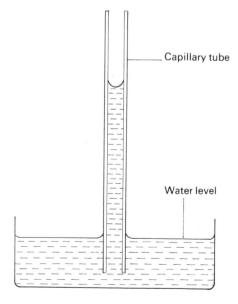

Figure 2.8 Water 'creeps' up the tube by capillary action

INVESTIGATION

THE NUMBER OF STOMATA

If a plant leaf on a slide is illuminated from above you can count the number of stomata. Observe and count the number of stomata for a fixed area (part of the field of view at low power) on both surfaces of a bean leaf and calculate the number of stomata per unit area.

Q Do the photomicrographs show the same number of stomata for a fixed area? Compare the results with those of an iris or grass leaf. Comment on any differences.

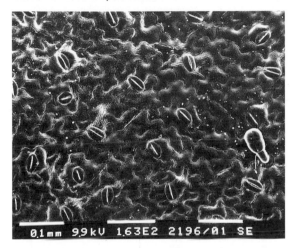

Upper epidermis of broad bean leaf (surface view)

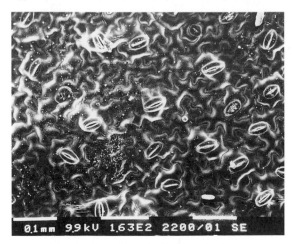

Lower epidermis of broad bean leaf (surface view)

Once in the leaf, water diffuses from the xylem vessels into all the cells where it has several functions. It is a raw material for photosynthesis. It acts as a medium for enzyme-catalysed reactions and for transport. It supports the leaf. Paradoxically, it is the loss of water from the stomata that ensures a continuous fresh supply to the plant! However, transpiration does need to be controlled because, if the loss exceeds the supply, cells lose water, become less turgid, and the plant *wilts* and is unable to photosynthesise. Under drought conditions, the stomata close, with the result that the supply of carbon dioxide for photosynthesis is also reduced. Some is, of course, produced as a result of respiration, but this situation cannot last. (Why not?) Depending on various factors, the stomata open and close, maintaining an appropriate balance between carbon dioxide uptake and water conservation. Plants growing in deserts must have adaptations to conserve water. They are known as *xerophytes*, as are sand dune plants like sand sedge (page 13), also growing where water is in short supply.

The stomatal pore is surrounded by two sausage-shaped *guard cells* in contact at their ends. Unlike the other epidermal cells, these cells usually contain chloroplasts. The guard cell walls are of unequal thickness, those nearer the pore being thicker and therefore less elastic than the opposite walls (Fig.2.9).

Photomicrograph of bean leaf stomata

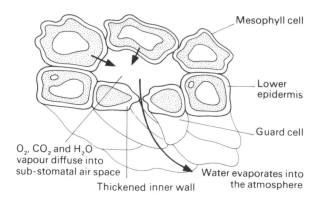

Mesophyll cell

Lower epidermis

Guard cell

O₂, CO₂ and H₂O vapour diffuse into sub-stomatal air space

Thickened inner wall

Water evaporates into the atmosphere

Figure 2.9 Stereodiagram to show the structure of a stoma as seen in the photomicrograph on page 23 (bottom right)

When the guard cells lose water, they become *flaccid* (limp). They collapse together and the stoma closes. When they gain water, the guard cells become turgid, the inner thicker walls resume their curved shape and, because the cells are joined at their ends, the stoma opens (Fig.2.10).

Explanations of the control of stomatal move-

a)

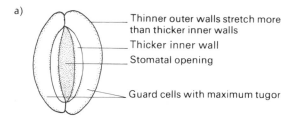

Thinner outer walls stretch more than thicker inner walls

Thicker inner wall

Stomatal opening

Guard cells with maximum tugor

b)

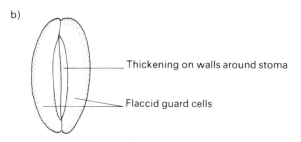

Thickening on walls around stoma

Flaccid guard cells

Figure 2.10 Stoma: a) open and b) closed

ment have changed over the years. Here we will take a typical situation. In the bean and most other plants, when there is enough water, stomata open during the day and close at night. The older explanation was no doubt suggested by the presence of chloroplasts in the guard cells. It seemed so simple! Illumination of these chloroplasts produced sugar, water moved into the guard cells by osmosis, so the stoma opened. However, careful research has shown that insufficient sugar is present in the guard cells during the day to influence its turgidity. Indeed, some plants open their stomata at night. It is now known that the concentration of potassium ions in the guard cells changes in response to light and these changes are large enough to draw in water and open the stomata.

We can now look at the rest of the leaf structure and its physiology. The broad bean has a *compound leaf* with three to seven leaflets (Fig.2.11a). Each leaflet is broad, increasing the surface area exposed to light, yet thin - minimising the distance over which carbon dioxide has to diffuse. Its shape and orientation is maintained by the turgidity of the cells and the presence of strengthening thick-walled tissue; sclerenchyma and xylem.

The whole leaf (Fig.2.11) is held together by the epidermis which forms a protective, binding layer on the outside, complete except for the stomata. The strength of this binding layer is increased in some species where the outline of these cells are jigsaw shaped, giving a bigger surface for their 'gluing together'.

The *chlorenchyma* of the leaf consists of parenchymatous mesophyll cells which contain *chloroplasts* (the oval structures containing chlorophyll) which trap light energy and start the photosynthetic processes. In the bean, the chlorenchyma is divided into *upper palisade* and *lower spongy mesophyll* (Fig.2.11c). The spongy appearance is due to the many interconnecting air spaces between the cells which provide a large surface area for gaseous exchange in both respiration and photosynthesis. Chlorenchyma cells are thin walled to allow easy diffusion, and their surfaces are moist to allow gases to dissolve before passing into the cells.

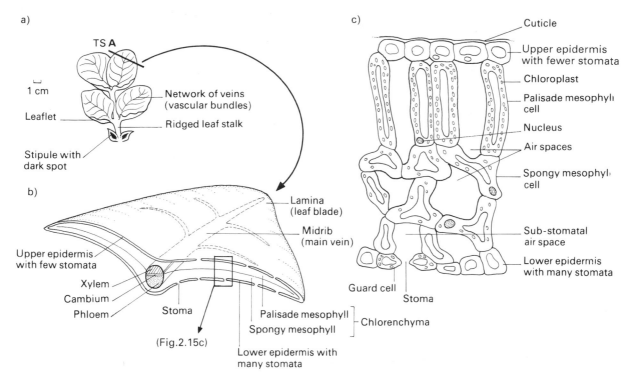

a)

TS **A**

⌐ ¬
1 cm

Leaflet

Stipule with
dark spot

Network of veins
(vascular bundles)

Ridged leaf stalk

b)

Upper epidermis
with few stomata

Xylem
Cambium
Phloem

Stoma

(Fig.2.15c)

Lamina
(leaf blade)

Midrib
(main vein)

Palisade mesophyll
Spongy mesophyll

Lower epidermis with
many stomata

Chlorenchyma

c)

Cuticle

Upper epidermis
with fewer stomata

Chloroplast

Palisade mesophyll
cell

Nucleus

Air spaces

Spongy mesophyll
cell

Sub-stomatal
air space

Lower epidermis
with many stomata

Guard cell

Stoma

Figure 2.11 Broad bean (*Vicia faba*): a) compound pinnate leaf, b) stereodiagram of part of a leaflet to illustrate the distribution of tissues, c) high power drawing of some cells in a transverse section

Q 1. The palisade cells have a greater concentration of chloroplasts than the spongy mesophyll. Why?

2. Chloroplasts migrate through the cell's cytoplasm. Sometimes they are concentrated along the vertical length of the cell, sometimes near the epidermal surface. Can you suggest a reason for this?

■ The manufacture of carbohydrates

Photosynthesis is the process by which carbon dioxide is taken up and assimilated into carbohydrates. The equation may be written as:

Carbon dioxide ⟶ Carbohydrate
+   Light   +
water   Chlorophyll   oxygen

But using chemical symbols it is usually written as:

$$6CO_2 + 6H_2O_6 \longrightarrow C_6H_{12}O_6 + 6O_2$$

Details of the biochemistry of the process are outside the scope of this book but are covered in *Biology Advanced Studies - Biochemistry*.

The *rate of photosynthesis* is affected by the availability of the raw materials, the presence of light and may also be affected by other environmental factors, such as temperature, herbicides and pollutants.

The present percentage of carbon dioxide in the air is usually given as 0.04%. If concentrations are increased up to about 0.1%, the rate of photosynthesis increases. Above that level the plant suffers damage, perhaps because it cannot cope with the increasing acidity.

Both the quality and the intensity of the light can effect the rate of photosynthesis. Not all wavelengths of light are equally active. Red and blue light trigger chlorophyll to lose an electron and start the photosynthetic process, green light does not. In a graph showing the rate of photosynthesis plotted against wavelength (an *action spectrum* - Fig.2.12) we see peaks of activity corresponding to the wavelengths of red and blue light. At low light intensity, there is no photosynthesis. It increases with an increase in light intensity as we can see clearly in 'starch-prints' of partially shaded leaves.

25

■ HOW TO MAKE A STARCH-PRINT

Potted geranium

Microslide

Microslide   Leaf   Black paper with cut-out design

Rubber band

1. Put the glass-paper sandwich on a living leaf. Leave for twenty-four hours in light.

2. Remove leaf from the plant and remove 'sandwich'

Boiling water

Leaf

Beaker

3. Immediately plunge leaf in boiling water for one minute to kill the leaf and to make the cells permeable.

If using a flame to boil water, turn out the Bunsen *before* using the methylated spirits.

Methylated spirits

Boiling water

4. Put the leaf in methylated spirits in a water bath until chlorophyll has left the leaf.

Area not exposed to light

Dropper

Tile

7. Blue-black colour appears on parts which were exposed to light.

6. Add iodine solution to the leaf on a white tile.

8. Use this technique to find out which tree species in your garden store starch in their leaves.

5. Wash the leaf under the tap.

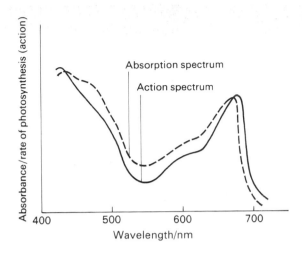

Figure 2.12 Action spectrum for photosynthesis compared with absorption spectrum of photosynthetic pigments

and are accessory pigments. *Phaeophytin* is a breakdown product of chlorophyll (see Investigation on page 28).

Variegated leaves occur naturally in some species and are favoured by gardeners for their decorative qualities, but the yellow areas lack chlorophyll and so cannot fix carbon dioxide. Such plants tend not to survive in the wild in competition with normal green varieties. Other factors that can reduce chlorophyll levels in a leaf include virus infections, mineral deficiency (e.g. iron and magnesium), and old age.

An increase in temperature increases the rate at which chemical reactions take place, as well as the rate of physical processes (e.g. diffusion) by speeding up the movement of molecules. The reactions in the photosynthetic chain are controlled by enzymes. In temperate plants, the

Variegated leaves of an ivy plant

If we check the absorption by leaf pigments of different wavelengths of light, we find that most is absorbed in the red and blue bands. This can be shown as an absorption spectrum (Fig.2.13). Note how closely this graph corresponds with that of the action spectrum (Fig.2.12). Chloroplasts contain a mixture of pigments, which can be separated by *chromatography*. Of these, the four most common are *chlorophylls* α and β which absorb red light and set off the photosynthetic process, and *xanthophyll* and *carotene* which absorb blue light

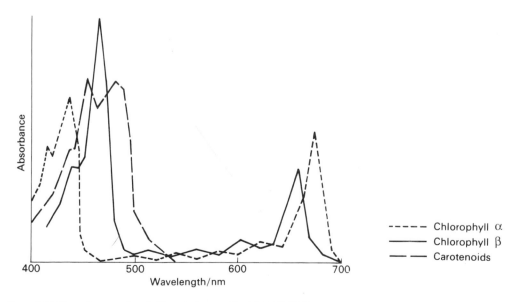

Chlorophyll α
Chlorophyll β
Carotenoids

Figure 2.13 Absorption spectra of chlorophylls α and β and carotenoids

INVESTIGATION

■ PLANT PIGMENTS

Plant pigments can be separated using chromatography. A solvent is made with one part acetone and nine parts petroleum ether.

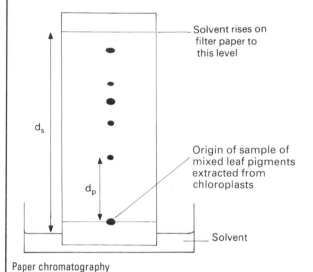

Paper chromatography

Once the pigments have been separated on chromatography paper they can be identified by calculating their R_f value as follows:

$$R_f = \frac{\text{distance moved by pigment}}{\text{distance moved by solvent}} = \frac{d_p}{d_s}$$

The R_f values of some common pigments are given in the table below.

Pigment	Color	P_f value
Carotene	Yellow	0.95
Phaeophytin	Yellow-grey	0.83
Xanthophyll	Yellow-brown	0.71
Chlorophyll a	Blue-green	0.65
Chlorophyll b	Green	0.45

Table 2.4

rate of photosynthesis increases with temperature until an *optimum* is reached (between 25-35°C). This is the 'best' temperature for maximum enzyme activity. Above the optimum, enzymes, made of protein, start to *denature* and become inactive.

Photosynthesis is a complex chain of reactions, each of which may be affected by any of the factors we described above. You could say that the result of a relay race is decided, not by the fastest runner but by the speed of the slowest. So although each factor affects the rate of photosynthesis independently it is the weakest one, operating below its optimum, which decides the overall rate. This factor is therefore called the *limiting factor* (Fig.2.14).

 What is the limiting factor in Fig.2.14?

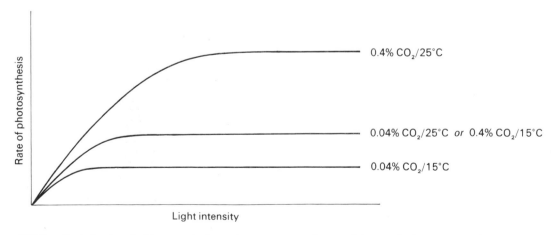

Figure 2.14 The effect of carbon dioxide concentration and temperature on the rate of photosynthesis

■ Mineral uptake

Minerals are dissolved in the soil water as a dilute solution of *ions* and it is only in the form of ions that they can be taken into the root cells.

As the concentration of ions is greater inside the cell than in the water, ions will not just diffuse in - energy has to be used to transport them against the concentration gradient. This uptake is called *active transport* and needs the energy provided by actively respiring cells. Once in the cells of the root, ions pass towards the xylem by diffusion or active transport, depending on their relative concentrations. The cells of the endodermis concentrate the incoming ions and selectively transport some so that the relative concentration of ions in the xylem can be very different from that in the soil solution.

---

ion an electrically charged atom or molecule.
For example, potassium nitrate exists in solution as:

$$KNO_3 \longrightarrow K^+ \text{ (cation)} + NO_3^- \text{ (anion)}$$

■ MINERALS ESSENTIAL TO THE GROWTH OF THE BROAD BEAN

For normal growth and development, all plants need certain essential elements. The figures in Table 2.2 show the concentration of these trace and major elements in the broad bean leaf, in parts per million (ppm), together with their functions.

Notice the huge range of concentrations of the elements. The major nutrients are part of the main structure and function of the plant, while the trace elements are required mainly as cofactors which must be present for certain enzyme reactions to occur.

Plants do not need soil to grow as long as they are provided with a dilute solution of all the essential elements in the appropriate proportions. Growing plants in such a solution is known as *hydroponics*. In plant culture experiments, the components of the solution are varied to obtain information about the role of these elements in the growth of the plant by observation of deficiency symptoms.

	Form	Concentration / ppm dry mass	Examples of function
Major elements			
Nitrogen	NO^{3-}	40 000	Component of protein
Phosphorus	PO_4^{3-}	2 000	Component of cell membrane and ATP
Potassium	K^+	10 000	Osmotic control
Calcium	Ca^2	20 000	Strengthening of cell walls
Magnesium	Mg^2	5 000	Component of chlorophyll
Sulphur	SO_4^{2-}	2 000	Component of protein
Trace elements			
Iron	Fe^{2+}	100	Chlorophyll synthesis, catalase
Manganese	Mn^{2+}	40	Respiration
Zinc	Zn^{2+}	25	Anaerobic respiration
Boron	BO_3^{3-}	20	Cell division, transport of sugars
Copper	Cu^{2+}	10	Cytochrome oxidase in respiration
Molybdenum	MoO_4^{2-}	1	Nitrate $\longrightarrow$ nitrite in amino acid synthesis, nitrogenase

Table 2.5

INVESTIGATION

■ TO DETERMINE THE EFFECTS OF NITROGEN, MAGNESIUM AND IRON ON THE GROWTH OF SEEDLINGS

Make up nutrient solutions using the quantities given below. Germinate some wheat (or other cereal) grains until the shoot is about 2cm tall. Wrap each of four seedlings in a bung of cotton wool and place it in a boiling tube containing enough of the solution to immerse the roots. Cover the outside of the tubes with foil or black paper and label them. As the solution is taken up by the plant, top up the level with distilled water.

Complete solution, (Knop's) control

0.8 g calcium nitrate
0.2 g potassium nitrate
0.2 g potassium dihydrogen phosphate
0.2 g magnesium phosphate
trace iron (III) phosphate
1 dm³ distilled water

Nitrogen-deficient

0.4 g potassium dihydrogen phosphate
0.2 g magnesium phosphate
0.6 g calcium sulphate
trace iron (III) phosphate
1 dm³ distilled water

Magnesium-deficient

0.8 g calcium nitrate
0.2 g potassium nitrate
0.2 g potassium dihydrogen phosphate
0.2 g calcium phosphate
trace iron (III) phosphate
1 dm³ distilled water

Iron-deficient

0.8 g calcium nitrate
0.2 g potassium nitrate
0.2 g potassium dihydrogen phosphate
0.2 g magnesium phosphate
1 dm³ distilled water

 1. Select and use a method for recording changes in growth of the shoot and root.

2. Observe and record changes in colour and growth habit.

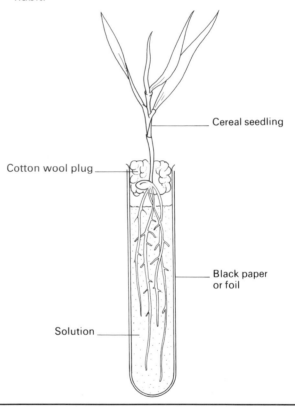

Cereal seedling

Cotton wool plug

Black paper or foil

Solution

Lack of nitrogen is the most common cause of poor growth. (Why?) However, it may be worth emphasising here that nitrates are not just a compound that comes in the farmer's fertiliser bag. If you look at Fig.2.15 you will see that nitrates are produced naturally by nitrifying bacteria, which use decomposed protein in the form of ammonia or nitrite as a source of energy. The amount of nitrate produced in this way is startling - about 50 million tonnes per year - equal to the total production of artificial nitrogen fertilisers!

In a natural habitat, when plants die, they decay and are thus recycled and their nutrients released into the soil. However, when a crop in a field is harvested, plant material is removed and lost to the recycling process and the level of nutrients in the soil decreases. Knowledge of the nutrient requirements of the crop and of the chemicals present in the soil should enable a farmer to top up these nutrients to the required level. However, the quantities of artificial fertilisers used in some areas have sometimes been in excess of the amounts needed.

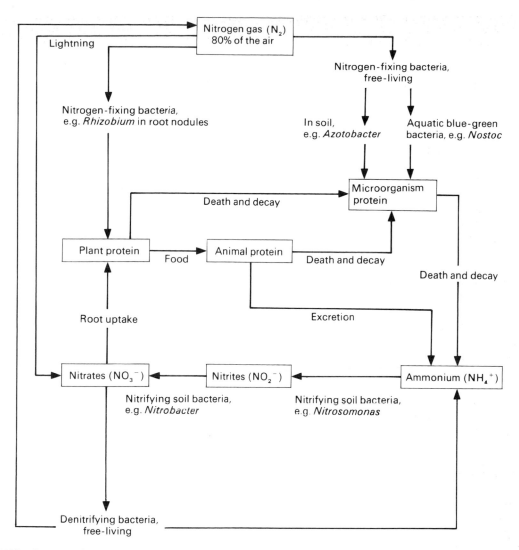

Figure 2.15 The nitrogen cycle

Excess nitrates are particularly worrying as they are very soluble and not held by soil particles, unlike potassium ions on clay, for example. Surplus nitrate leaches from the soil, into streams, rivers and reservoirs and finally into the sea. Some will find its way into underground aquifers where it stays as nitrate, to contaminate drinking water at a later date. Excess nitrates in drinking water are believed to be harmful to humans, and may cause mental abnormality in babies. An increase in nitrates in ponds and lakes, an example of *eutrophication*, causes the rapid growth of water weeds and algae called an algal bloom. In late summer, these plants die, increasing the *biological oxygen demand* (BOD). Oxygen is used up by aerobic bacteria, lowering the oxygen content of the water and so killing susceptible animals. Finally, only the anaerobic decomposing bacteria and animals which come to the surface to breathe can survive.

■ LEGUMES ARE SPECIAL!

The bacterium *Rhizobium leguminosarum* provides the broad bean, and other members of the Leguminosae family, with its own private supply of nitrogen fertiliser. How does this happen? The bacterium, which is present in most soils, invades the root hairs of bean seedlings, multiplies rapidly and produces swellings (*nodules*) on the roots

These nodules develop vascular connections with the plant root (Fig.2.16). The bacteria live in a *symbiotic* relationship with the bean. It supplies the bacteria with sucrose from its phloem and receives the organic nitrogenous compound fixed by the bacteria from nitrogen in the soil air. Young active nodules are pink in colour owing to the presence of *leghaemoglobin*, similar, but not identical to, the pigment in mammalian blood.

Nodules on *Vicia faba* root

Q A single bean plant may bear up to 1000 nodules. In Fig.2.16 there is no epidermis and the nodule is open and spongy. What is the advantage of this?

The nodule bacteria make the enzyme *nitrogenase* (containing the trace elements iron and molybdenum) which catalyses the reduction of gaseous nitrogen to ammonia as shown in the equation below.

$$N_2 + 6H^+ + 6e^- \longrightarrow 2NH_3$$
$$ATP \qquad ADP$$

The reaction involves oxidative phosphorylation and ATP, while the reducing power (e^-) comes from the respiration of sucrose supplied by the bean. Oxygen is essential and its concentration is regulated by leghaemoglobin.

Ammonia is not used as such by the plant (it is poisonous). It is immediately linked in the roots with one amino acid (*aspartic acid*) to form another, *asparagine* (Fig.2.17). Asparagine is the main nitrogenous compound transported in the xylem of a broad bean plant with nodules.

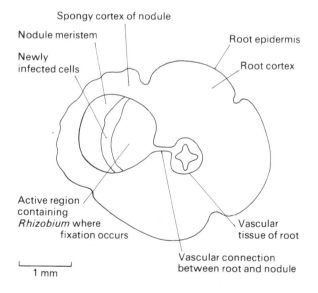

Figure 2.16 Transverse section of *Vicia faba* root with a nodule

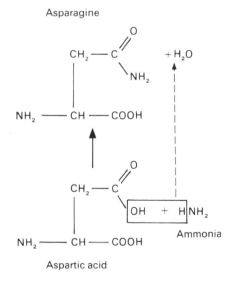

Figure 2.17 The formation of asparagine from aspartic acid in *Vicia faba* roots

Scanning electron micrographs of a transverse section of a broad bean (*Vicia faba*) stem.
The same preparation was used for all photographs but the magnification was increased:
a) x 11, b) x 57, c) x 170, d) x 2100.

The ability of leguminous plants to grow well without added manure was observed long before the action of nodule bacteria was understood. A legume, usually clover, was included in the classical four part *crop rotation* introduced as part of the agricultural revolution in Britain in the eighteenth century. Analysis has since shown that the level of nitrates in the soil increases after the roots of the clover have decayed. At Rothamsted Experimental Station (UK), it was found that the yield of wheat, in a field in which beans had been grown the year before, was about 50% greater than in a similar field where wheat followed another wheat crop. (For some years a serious attempt has been made to find the nitrogen-fixing gene and transfer it from leguminous plants into other plants. They would then be able to make their own nitrate fertiliser!)

Q What are the advantages and disadvantages of adding chemical nitrate fertiliser to soil?

Nowadays, *Vicia faba* beans are grown widely, mainly as a 'break crop' to interrupt the cycles of cereal disease organisms (*pathogens*) in the soil, whilst at the same time providing a valuable alternative crop.

■ TRANSPORT

The vascular bundles or veins are the transport system of a bean (Figs.1.7, 2.2). *Phloem sieve tubes* are elongated cells joined end to end, but

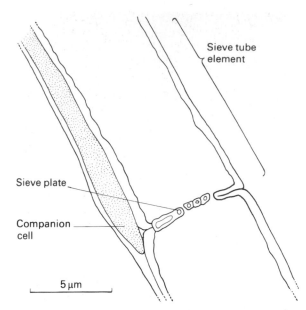

Figure 2.18 Vertical section of a phloem sieve tube and companion cell

unlike xylem vessels, the end walls remain and are perforated by many small pores to form a *sieve plate* (Fig.1.7, 2.18). The cytoplasm, which includes cell organelles but no nucleus, lies close to the cell walls. There are long fine strands of protein running through the sieve plate pores from one cell to the next. Beside each sieve tube cell is a companion cell with dense living contents including a nucleus and many mitochondria. *Companion cells* are active and supply energy to the sieve tubes (Fig.2.18). The xylem carries water and minerals

(and asparagine in beans) from the roots to the leaves in the xylem vessels. The phloem carries food (the products of photosynthesis) up and down the plant in the sieve tubes, depending on where it is required. Transporting food in this way is known as *translocation*. To be moved, the food must be soluble; once it reaches a storage tissue it is converted into an insoluble form. (Why?) The main substance translocated in the phloem of beans is sucrose. There are also amino acids, organic acids, mineral ions, vitamins and plant growth substances. Large quantities of assimilated substances are moved rapidly, both upwards and downwards, though not in the same tube. (Remember, xylem flow is always upwards.) The process is called *mass flow*, that is, the water and the solute molecules move together in the same direction, as distinct from diffusion where these molecules move independently and not necessarily in the same direction. In its simplest form it is suggested that phloem movement is driven by a gradient in the pressure potentials going from a *source* (e.g. the leaves), down to a *sink* for use or storage (e.g. the roots). Once initiated, this gradient would set up a passive mass flow of solution between the leaves and roots. This model (Fig.2.19) originally proposed by Münch in 1930, would result in mass flow, but there are doubts as to whether this theory alone would account for the high rate and quantity of movement. Subsequent modifications to this theory include a) movement of potassium ions (*electro-osmosis*) around the sieve plate and b) active streaming of molecules along the surface of the protein strands running through the sieve pores.

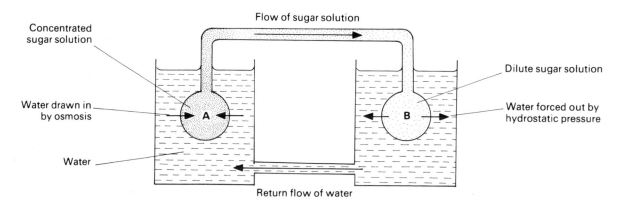

Figure 2.19 The principle of the mass flow hypothesis. Two reservoirs, A and B, have partially-permeable walls and are connected together with a tube to form a sealed system. Both A and B contain sugar solution, A being more concentrated than B. When the reservoirs are immersed in beakers of water, water is drawn into A by osmosis, setting up a flow of sugar from A to B. The increased pressure in B forces water out into the beaker. This mass flow will continue as long as the sugar concentration in A is greater than that in B.

Evidence for the transport of the food assimilated by a plant can be obtained from experiments using radioactive carbon dioxide. If a leaf is exposed to $^{14}CO_2$ for only a few minutes and then left in contact with a photographic film, the resulting picture (*autoradiograph*) shows darkened areas indicating the presence of radioactive carbon compounds. These areas correspond to the position of the phloem, not only in the leaf but also in sections of leaf stalk and stem. Similar experiments have shown that food made in photosynthesis is translocated to the developing pod where it is stored in the cotyledons in an insoluble form for the later development of the embryo.

Some parasitic animals and plants make use of the nutrients in the phloem. The bean aphid or black fly (*Aphis fabae*) is a well-known insect pest. It feeds by inserting its *stylet* (mouth parts) through the epidermis into a phloem sieve tube with great precision. Experiments have been done using a different species, where, having established the aphid on a plant, it is killed by using solid carbon dioxide and the body removed, leaving the stylet in place. This can then be used as a miniature hypodermic needle enabling samples from one phloem sieve tube to be taken for analysis. These delicate experiments have demonstrated what substances are carried in solution and the speed of phloem transport.

■ GROWTH AND YIELD

Growth involves changes in the number, size and differentiation of cells and results in an increase in height, or length, area, volume, dry mass or protein content. Note that in our definition of growth on page 15 we refer to 'dry mass'. However, an increase in wet mass can also occur with uptake of water. Unfortunately, drying a plant to weigh it, kills it!

There are various ways of measuring the growth of a plant, some of which are described here.

■ Measuring height or length
The height of a plant can be measured at intervals using computer monitoring with sensors and data logging, or using time-lapse photography to record the changes. However, this does not take account of growth in other directions, e.g. side shoots and expanding leaves.

$^{14}CO_2$ carbon dioxide made from a heavy isotope of carbon called carbon fourteen, ^{14}C

Computer monitoring with sensors which record the changes in plant height and, by means of data-logging software, stores the information at timed intervals

■ Measuring volume
This method should provide a good indication of the growth of the whole plant but is not at all easy to carry out in practice!

■ Measuring area
The size of a leaf can be measured by outlining it on graph paper and calculating the enclosed area. If this is done with the leaf still attached to the plant, measurements can be made at intervals to demonstrate change in size.

■ Using dry mass
This is the accepted method for giving the most accurate results. A large number of similar plants are needed at the beginning of an experiment so that adequate numbers can be removed at intervals to dry and weigh, using carefully reproducible conditions. For each batch weighed, a mean mass can be calculated. If these mean values are plotted against time, a growth curve is obtained (Fig.2.20a). This is a typical S-shaped curve, showing *absolute growth*. Growth appears to be slow initially until the leaves are established, when it increases. As the plant matures, growth slows down again. The rate of growth is measured by the slope of the absolute growth curve at any one time. If the change in size or mass from one time interval to the next is plotted, a *growth rate* curve is obtained (Fig.2.20b). A better picture of what is actually happening is shown by plotting the growth, expressed as a percentage of the growth that has

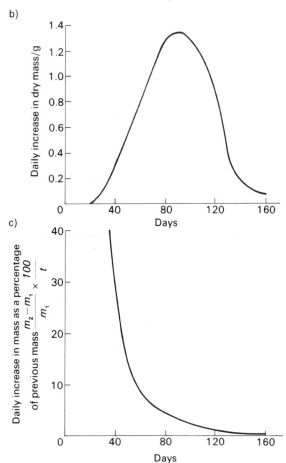

already taken place, against time. This is known as the *relative growth rate* (Fig.2.20c) and it shows that growth is fast in the young plant but slows down with age.

Combinations of these methods can give other useful information:

• *Net assimilation rate (NAR)* is the rate of increase in dry mass of the whole plant per unit area of leaf. NAR gives an idea of the photosynthetic efficiency of a species. This could be valuable in deciding which crops produce the greatest biomass.

• *Leaf area index (LAI)* is the ratio of leaf area to the dry mass of the whole plant.

Both NAR and LAI can be used to compare growth rates under different environmental conditions, for example, shade and sun.

The relative growth rate is the net assimilation rate multiplied by the leaf area index.

Q 1. Devise an experimental method for investigating the growth of broad bean seedlings using volume.

2. Devise and set up a long-term experiment to record relative growth rates of bean and barley seedlings. Assess their value as green crops.

■ THE BROAD BEAN AS A CROP

For both human food and animal fodder, the beans are extracted from the pods, as most of the food is stored in the seed. The mass of the beans expressed as a percentage of the mass of the whole plant is known as the *harvestable dry matter*. Table 2.6 shows the foods present in the broad bean.

Food type	Percentage
Sugars	5.5
Starch	41.4
Hemicellulose	5.6
Cellulose	8.0
Lignin	1.5
Total carbohydrate	62.0
Total protein	32.5
Total lipid	1.6
Total minerals	3.5
TOTAL	99.6

Figure 2.20 Growth of *Vicia faba*: a) absolute growth curve, b) growth rate curve, c) relative growth rate curve

Table 2.6 Percentage food composition of the broad bean

Continent	Production / tons $\times 10^3$	Main producers / tons $\times 10^3$
Africa	716	Ethiopia (277), Egypt (262), Morocco (65)
North and Central America	97	Mexico (79), no figures available for Canada
South America	115	Brazil (62)
Asia	2791	China (2700), no figures for Afghanistan, Iran, India, Pakistan
Europe	647	Italy (206), UK (122), Czechoslovakia (71)
Australasia	15	
World total	c 4400	

Table 2.7 World production of the broad bean   Source: FAO 1981

For use as a vegetable, the plants are harvested when the seeds are still immature and then used fresh, canned or frozen. They are particularly valuable in a vegetarian diet because of their high protein level and for their dietary fibre. The amino acid content of bean protein is similar to that of meat, except that the quantity of the sulphur-containing amino acids is less, but there is more lysine. This is the reverse of the situation in cereals, therefore a mixture of beans and cereals gives a good balance - beans on toast! In some poorer countries, notably the Middle East, the mature dried bean seed is crushed and cooked as a staple food (Table 2.7).

In Britain beans are also used as the starting point for the manufacture of textured vegetable protein, in place of the usual source, imported soya bean extract.

The broad bean as we know it is a variety of *Vicia faba* that has been bred to produce larger seeds (mass 1.5-2 g) than the field bean grown for animal feed (0.2-0.5 g) but this smaller mass is offset by the fact that more pods are produced. Ninety per cent of the total *Vicia faba* grown in Britain is for fodder. When mature the plants are harvested and the dry seeds are threshed out using a standard cereal combine. The roots, with their nodules, are left to enrich the soil.

■ OTHER IMPORTANT LEGUMINOUS CROPS

The other familiar beans grown in Britain belong to the genus *Phaseolus* which originated in South America but is now found almost all over the world. The scarlet runner bean is *Phaseolus coccineus*, while the variously named dwarf, French and haricot bean is *P. vulgaris*. Vast quantities of a variety of *P. vulgaris*, known as navy beans, are grown in the USA to satisfy our demand for baked beans in tomato sauce.

Seed size varies widely from the large butter bean (*P. lunatus*) to the small mung bean (*P. aureus*). Mung bean seeds are germinated in the dark to form bean sprouts.

Peas are probably the most popular frozen vegetable in Britain, and their cultivation and harvesting are now closely regulated by the food production companies. In contrast, the lentil is rarely grown here, although the seed is widely available. It is an ancient crop, originating in the Mediterranean region. For centuries the seed's high protein content has been valued, especially in some Catholic countries where meat may not be eaten during Lent.

With minor exceptions, all the above plants grow and develop like *Vicia faba*. There are other legumes, however, which are very different in their growth habit or in their metabolism. The fat (lipid) content of the broad bean seed is low while about 60% is carbohydrate (see Table 2.6). In contrast, in soya bean seeds, most carbon is stored as lipid and little as carbohydrate, while the protein content can be as great or greater than that of broad beans. In peanuts too, the reserve carbon is present as lipid, up to 50% of the dry mass of the seed. Fruit growth here is unusual in that, after pollination, the flower stalks elongate downwards, taking the young pods below the ground surface to complete their development, hence the other name for this plant, groundnut (Fig.2.21). The lipids in both soya beans and peanuts contain mainly unsaturated fatty acids, which are of great commercial value for the manufacture of margarine and cooking oil, and are much in demand in this health conscious age. Both carbohydrate and lipid have the same function, to act as a source of energy in seed germination.

After studying of this chapter, you will know a great deal about plants in general, mainly through the study of one species. It will be important for you to look for similar and contrasting features in other plants that are available for your investigations in the laboratory and field.

Answer to question on page 20.
Did you get it right? –800 is higher than –1200 so water moves from cell B to cell A.

Figure 2.21 Groundnut plant (*Arachis hypogea*) showing pod production below ground and peanuts in the pod

WHAT'S IN A FLOWER?

CHAPTER 3

■ EVOLUTION OF FLOWERS

During the late Devonian period, some 400 million years ago, the first angiosperms colonised the land surface which was already dominated by ferns, clubmosses and horsetails. The flowering plants made little impact until the Cretaceous period when there was a great increase, coinciding with the appearance of the main groups of *pollinating* insects (Fig.3.1). We believe that angiosperms and

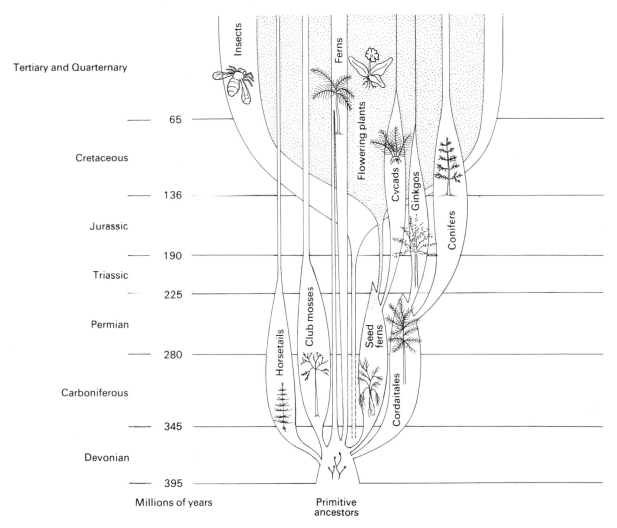

Figure 3.1 Evolution of flowering plants and insects. Insects have been in existence since the Devonian times. 350 million years ago they appeared as wingless animals. The groups so essential to plants: Hymenoptera (bees and wasps), Lepidoptera (moths and butterflies) and Diptera (flies), developed during the Triassic, Jurassic and Cretaceous times from ancestors which arose throughout the Carboniferous and Permian. It was during this time before the Cretaceous era that the close associations between insects and flowers must have arisen

insects have evolved alongside each other since there are instances of plants whose survival depends totally on a particular species of insect (e.g. each one of several hundred species of fig tree relies on its own species of gall wasp for pollination). It is thought that the original pollinators may have been beetles scrambling over the flowers in search of pollen for food; later, the *nectary* evolved, the sweet nectar attracting a larger range of insects. Perhaps, originally, nectaries served a different purpose. The phloem sieve tubes, carrying food away from the leaves, cannot function if the concentration of sugar in them is too high. (Why not?) The surplus sugar is extracted and stored in nectaries either inside the flower (e.g. buttercup) or outside (e.g. the glands at the leaf bases of busy Lizzie (Fig.3.2). If, in ancient angiosperms, such sugar glands were present, then insects would have been attracted to the flowers.

Evolutionary changes have gradually produced today's range of flowers with their differences in colour, and the relative position of nectaries, anthers and stigmas which attract insects with a particular design of feeding mouth parts (Fig.3.3).

a) Honeysuckle is protandrous
(anthers ripen before carpels)

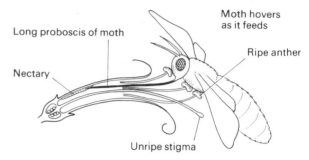

(i) Hawk moth picking up pollen from ripe anthers

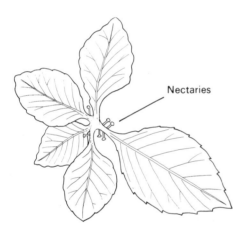

Figure 3.2 Extra-floral nectaries in busy Lizzie (*Impatiens* sp.)

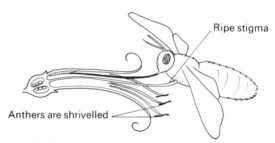

(ii) Hawk moth depositing pollen on ripe stigma

We can also imagine the evolution of scent and colour. Some plants produce scent that attracts insects either because it mimics their preferred food or their **pheromones**. The phenomenon of a fly which tries to mate with an orchid is well documented. Poinsettia (an attractive house plant at Christmas time) has large red bracts which attract insects, the flowers themselves being small and insignificant.

> **nectary** a glandular swelling, which can be within or external to the flower, that produces sugar nectar
>
> **pheromones** volatile substances produced in minute quantities by one sex and recognised by the other, so promoting mating

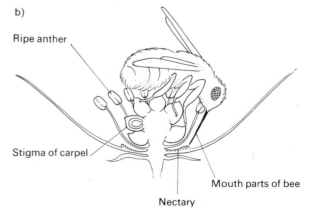

Figure 3.3 Pollinating insects: a) hawk moths on honeysuckle (*lonicera periclymenum*) and b) bee in buttercup (*Ranunculus* sp.)

Describe how the bee and hawk moth effect pollination.

Single flower heads of Christmas cactus

In general, large showy flowers are found singly, while small insignificant flowers tend to be massed into a flowering head or *inflorescence*, e.g. the umbel of angelica or carrot. The ultimate in close contact is seen in the family Compositeae where the so-called 'flower' is really an inflorescence made up of many tiny flowers or *florets*. For example, a daisy has an outer ring of white *ray florets* with a centre of tiny yellow *disc florets*.

 1. Examine with a hand lens the florets of a daisy and make drawings of their structure.

Florets of a daisy

An inflorescence of angelica

2. If large quantities of insecticide continue to be used, what implications are there for angiosperm survival?

We can see a link between the behaviour of insects and flowers. Insects are most active in warm sunshine when flowers are most likely to be in full bloom. Pollen in most land plants is less effective when wet, so some flowers do not open in dull and wet weather. The scarlet pimpernel only opens its petals in sunlight, an example of a *nastic response*, a non-directional movement in response to a stimulus. The stimulus may be light (*photonasty*) or temperature (*thermonasty*).

Look closely at the petals of some flowers and you will see that the colour is not uniform, there are streaks, spots or patches leading the eye to the base of the petal where the nectary is. These are the *honey guides* (Fig.3.4) which may show up as a totally different colour under ultraviolet light. Even the apparently uniform colour of a yellow buttercup shows guide lines clearly under such light.

We know that a large number of insects can see colour in the ultraviolet range and bees can see yellow and blue as well. For example, bees see yellow broom flowers as yellow with 'bee-purple' lines radiating from the centre of the flower. Of the insects that have been investigated, butterflies are apparently unique in being able to see red.

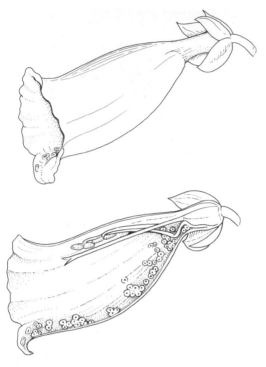

Figure 3.4 Foxglove (*Digitalis purpurea*). The spots on the petals act as honey guides

Honey guides of evening primrose seen under UV light

Typical insect-pollinated flower	Typical wind-pollinated flower
Conspicuous colour in petals, stamens or bracts	No bright colour, usually green, petals may be absent
Scented	Not scented
Nectaries present	Nectaries absent
Stamens enclosed within flower	Pendulous, long-filamented stamens hanging outside flower
Anthers fixed by their bases or fused along the back, immovable	Versatile anthers, attached at mid-point so they rock in air currents
Less pollen produced	Large amounts of pollen produced
Pollen large-grained, sticky, heavy, often with sculptured surface	Pollen small-grained, dry, light, often smooth surfaced
Small, sticky stigma, enclosed within flower	Large branched or feathery stigma hanging outside flower
Flower modified structurally for insects to land and feed	Flower structure relatively simple

Table 3.1

In addition, the surface epidermis of petals may be variously sculptured into knobs and ridges which affects the way light is reflected and hence the colour. They may also provide a foothold for insects and prevent the wetting of the surface and damage to the thin petals.

We know from fossil remains that some of the oldest flowering plants were insect-pollinated (*entomophilous*). It is likely that wind–pollinated (*anemophilous*) flowers, e.g. the grass family (Gramineae) with their anthers and feathery stigmas exposed to the slightest breeze, show a later evolutionary development (Fig.3.5).

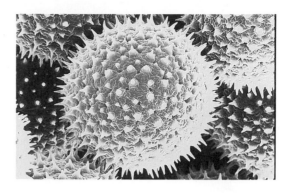

a)

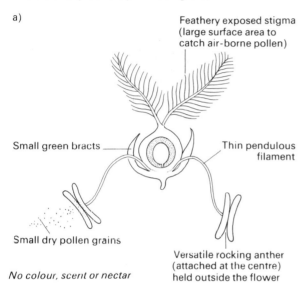

Feathery exposed stigma (large surface area to catch air-borne pollen)

Small green bracts

Thin pendulous filament

Small dry pollen grains

Versatile rocking anther (attached at the centre) held outside the flower

No colour, scent or nectar

b)

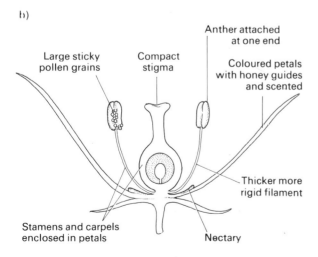

Large sticky pollen grains

Compact stigma

Anther attached at one end

Coloured petals with honey guides and scented

Thicker more rigid filament

Stamens and carpels enclosed in petals

Nectary

Figure 3.5 Vertical section of: a) a typical wind–pollinated flower (anemophilous), b) a typical insect–pollinated flower (entomophilous)

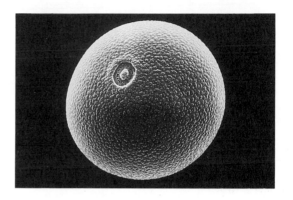

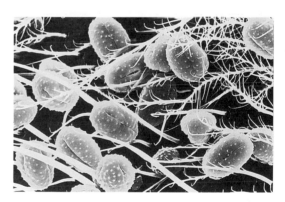

Scanning electron micrographs of pollen grains from different plant species

Q Look at the photomicrographs above. Which grains come from insect-pollinated flowers and which from wind-pollinated flowers? (Answers at the end of this chapter.)

■ THE LIFE CYCLE OF A TERRESTRIAL ANGIOSPERM

The diagram of the life cycle of a flowering plant (Fig.3.6) appears rather more complicated than the human life cycle! Flowers have inherited the remains of a two-stage cycle from primitive plants similar to present day ferns. The two stages (generations) depend on the number of chromosomes in the nuclei of the cells:

• The *sporophyte generation* has chromosomes in homologous pairs (*homo* = same, bearing the same range of characters). This we call the *diploid number* ($2n$). This stage has resulted from the fusion of sex cells or gametes in sexual reproduction to form a diploid embryo.

• The *gametophyte generation* has just one of each pair of chromosomes, so each cell has half the diploid number, i.e. the *haploid* number (n). Any cells formed as a result of a reduction division - *meiosis* - must be part of the gametophyte stage (Fig.3.7).

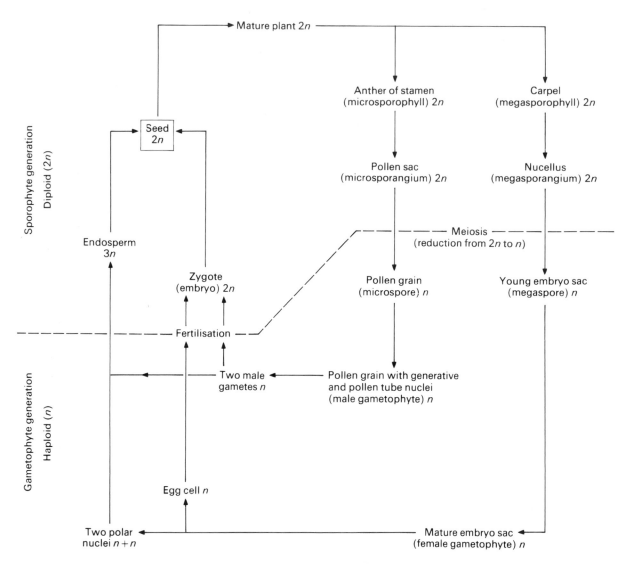

Figure 3.6 Angiosperm life cycle. Start examining this cycle at the seed stage and note that it and the mature plant have the diploid number ($2n$) of chromosomes in each cell. The male and female gametes have only the haploid number (n). Note that as well as the usual fertilisation (egg cell + male gamete) there is a second fertilisation where a male gamete fuses with another *two* nuclei derived from the female gametophyte. This is typical of all angiosperms

The sporophyte generation (2*n*) is the plant and the flowers. The gametophyte generation (*n*) is much reduced, consisting of just the pollen grain and ovule, which develop in the flowers. If you refer to Fig.3.7, you can see how the names used in the angiosperm life cycle match up with terms, such as 'spore', used in other plant groups.

The parts of a flower are usually arranged as shown in Fig.3.8. This diagram can be used to interpret the structures found in the main flower families, four of which are illustrated in Fig.3.9 (see also Appendix 1).

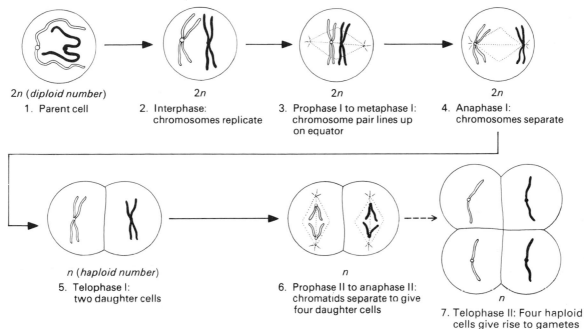

2*n* (*diploid number*)
1. Parent cell

2*n*
2. Interphase: chromosomes replicate

2*n*
3. Prophase I to metaphase I: chromosome pair lines up on equator

2*n*
4. Anaphase I: chromosomes separate

n (*haploid number*)
5. Telophase I: two daughter cells

n
6. Prophase II to anaphase II: chromatids separate to give four daughter cells

n
7. Telophase II: Four haploid cells give rise to gametes

Figure 3.7 The main events in meiosis, the reduction division. (Note that one pair of chromosomes only are shown)

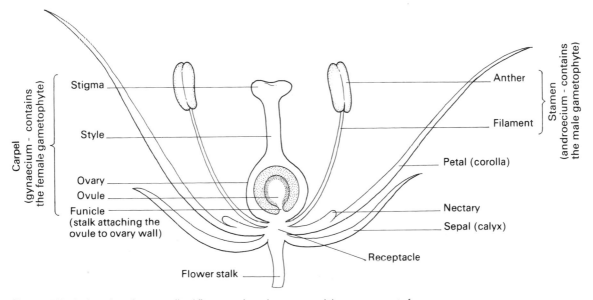

Carpel (gynaecium - contains the female gametophyte)

Stigma

Style

Ovary

Ovule

Funicle (stalk attaching the ovule to ovary wall)

Flower stalk

Anther

Filament

Stamen (androecium - contains the male gametophyte)

Petal (corolla)

Nectary

Sepal (calyx)

Receptacle

Figure 3.8 Vertical section of a generalised flower to show the names and the arrangement of the parts. The collective terms are shown in brackets. (Note the variations in flower parts found in the families illustrated in Fig. 3.9)

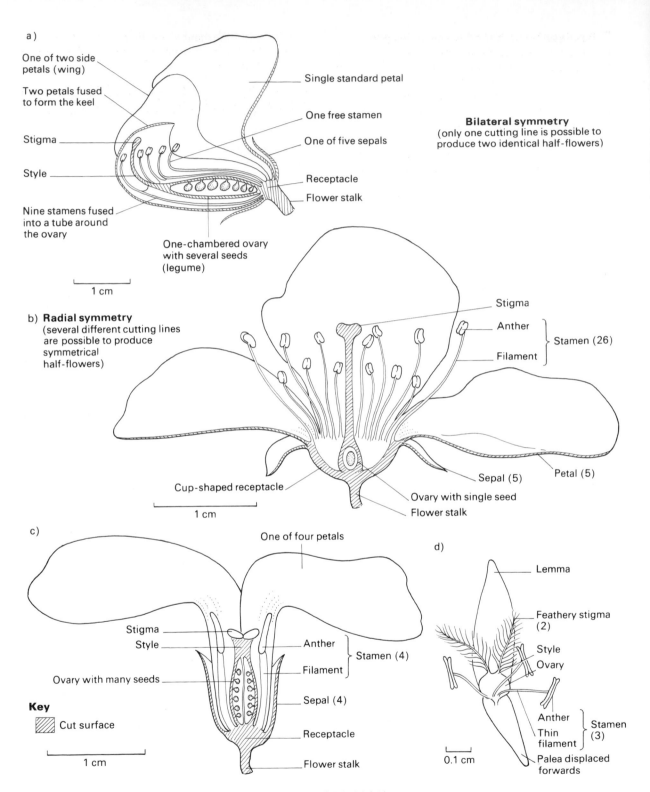

a)

One of two side petals (wing)

Two petals fused to form the keel

Stigma

Style

Nine stamens fused into a tube around the ovary

Single standard petal

One free stamen

One of five sepals

Receptacle

Flower stalk

One-chambered ovary with several seeds (legume)

Bilateral symmetry
(only one cutting line is possible to produce two identical half-flowers)

1 cm

b) **Radial symmetry**
(several different cutting lines are possible to produce symmetrical half-flowers)

Stigma

Anther

Filament

Stamen (26)

Sepal (5)

Petal (5)

Cup-shaped receptacle

Ovary with single seed

Flower stalk

1 cm

c)

One of four petals

Stigma

Style

Ovary with many seeds

Anther

Filament

Stamen (4)

Sepal (4)

Receptacle

Flower stalk

Key

Cut surface

1 cm

d)

Lemma

Feathery stigma (2)

Style

Ovary

Anther

Thin filament

Stamen (3)

Palea displaced forwards

0.1 cm

Figure 3.9 Vertical sections of flowers of: a) Leguminoseae, broad bean (*Vicia faba*), b) Rosaceae, plum (*Prunus* sp.), c) Crucifereae, wallflower (*Cheiranthus* sp.), d) Gramineae, meadow fescue grass (*Festuca pratensis*)

Development of the anther and pollen grain

Food and water is carried to the developing anther through a vascular bundle. The tissue differentiates into four double-walled pollen sacs, the *microsporangia,* capable of *dehiscence* (bursting open) at maturity. Inside the sacs, the *archesporial* ('first sowing') *tissue* develops into *pollen grains (microspores)* (Fig.3.10).

Each diploid *pollen (spore) mother cell* divides by meiosis to form a tetrad of haploid pollen grains (microspores). Walls form around the grain, a thick, sculptured outer layer, the *exine* with pores,

and a thin inner layer, the *intine.* Inside, the nucleus divides by mitosis to form *generative* and *pollen tube* nuclei.

INVESTIGATION

Pollen grains (e.g. *spider wort*) can be grown to produce pollen tubes in a petri dish on the surface of a sucrose solution (usually 0.3M, but this varies for different species). Find the optimum concentration for the pollen you test.

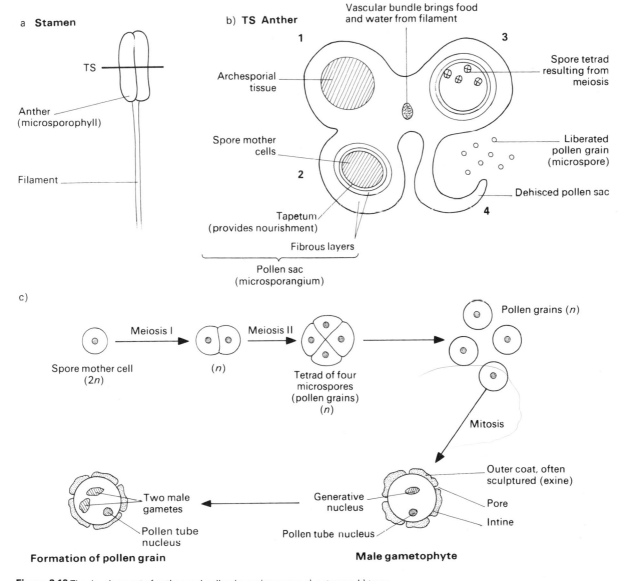

Figure 3.10 The development of anther and pollen in angiosperms: a) a stamen, b) transverse section of an anther, c) formation of a pollen grain

■ Development of the carpel and ovule

The number of *ovules* that develop within the ovary will depend on the species. The broad bean contains several in a row in the pod. The ovule is enclosed by protective layers of cells (*integuments*) which have a small opening, the *micropyle*, and are attached to the ovary wall by a short stalk (*funicle*). The *embryo sac* or *megasporangium* develops within the ovule. The *embryo sac mother cell* ($2n$) divides meiotically into four haploid cells, three of which degenerate. The fourth will develop into the embryo sac (the female gametophyte - Fig.3.11). The embryo sac (n) divides by mitosis to produce eight nuclei. Of these, only the egg cell nucleus and the two polar nuclei have a further part to play in fertilisation. The two *synergids* support the egg cell in the most suitable position but the three *antipodal* cells have no further function.

■ Pollination

When the pollen grains are ripe, the anther dries out setting up tensions in its wall which splits lengthwise, exposing the pollen grains either to be blown away or carried away by insects.

The pollen grains land on any stigma which is sticky with secreted sugar. However, pollen grains only start to grow if the stigma is of a compatible plant (usually the same species). The stigma produces *auxins* (plant growth substances) which stimulate a pollen tube to grow out through a pore in the exine and penetrate the tissue of the style by secreting digestive enzymes controlled by the *tube nucleus* at the growing tip. Auxins secreted by the carpel also stimulate the growth of the tube and its direction is chemically controlled (*chemotropism*). During this tube growth, the *generative cell* divides mitotically into two male, non-motile nuclei which

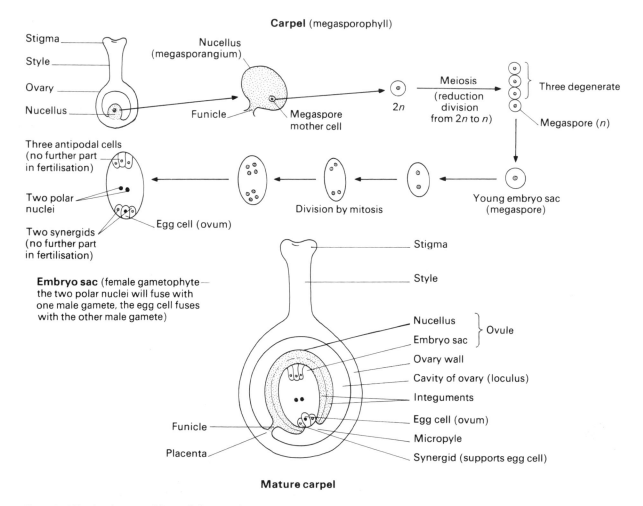

Figure 3.11 The development of the ovule in an angiosperm

are carried in the pollen tube into the ovary and through the micropyle. Here the tube nucleus breaks down and the tip of the tube bursts, liberating the *male nuclei* (Fig.3.12).

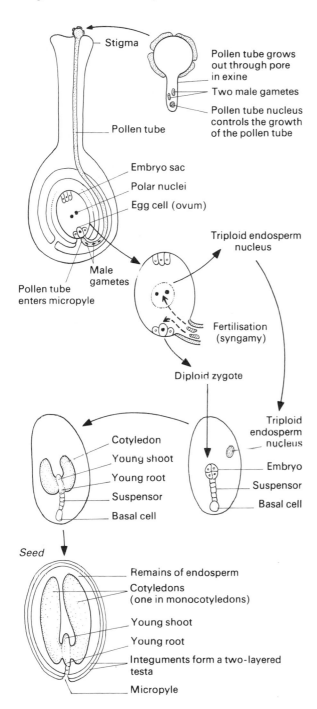

Figure 3.12 Fertilisation and the formation of the embryo in an angiosperm

Fertilisation

Pollination is followed by *fertilisation* where one of the two male nuclei (*gametes*) carried through the micropyle to the ovule fuses with the egg cell (*ovum*) to form a diploid *zygote*. The other fuses with the two *polar nuclei* (Fig.3.12) to form an unusual chromosome state - the *triploid* (3n) *endosperm* - which may develop to form the main food store in some endospermic seeds, e.g. maize. In non-endospermic seeds (e.g. broad bean) the main food store is within the cotyledons. It is this double fertilisation involving two male gametes that triggers off the formation of the endosperm. Since this process is energy-consuming it is an advantage to the plant to avoid it if fertilisation does not occur. Fertilisation following *cross-pollination* (outbreeding) has the advantage that the genes or characters from different parents come together. This produces varied offspring which are often stronger and healthier, a phenomenon known as *hybrid vigour*. Too much inbreeding (*self-fertilisation*) tends to bring unfavourable genes together.

However, many plants do self-fertilise if cross-pollination has not taken place, e.g. dandelions. It is better to get some seed than none at all! However, inbreeding can be used to an advantage in the production of F_1 *hybrids*. Plants selected for particular characteristics are self-pollinated for at least seven generations, producing offspring with a uniform appearance (*phenotype*) but which are often weak and small. Seeds produced from crossing these parents produce the typically vigorous hybrids, such as many new varieties of garden flowers and vegetables. These F_1 plants, however, will not breed true. They produce either sterile or very variable seeds, so you will need to buy a new packet of F_1 seeds each year!

Many adaptations exist which prevent self-pollination in the wild:
• Anthers and carpels may ripen at different times (*dichogamy*), e.g. rosebay willowherb and dandelion are *protandrous* (anthers shed their pollen before the carpels are ripe). *Protogyny*, when the carpels ripen first, is less common. Honeysuckle and bluebell are protogynous.
• The relative positions of the flower parts may help to prevent self-pollination, e.g. the primrose (Fig.3.13), where the styles may be long (pin-eyed) or short (thrum-eyed).
• In some species the anthers and carpels may be in different flowers, either on the same (*monoecious*) or different (*dioecious*) plants. Among monoecious species are important food crops, e.g. maize, marrows and cucumbers. Dioecious species include

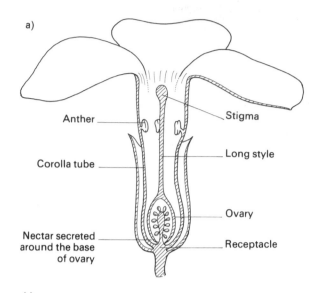

a)

Anther

Stigma

Corolla tube

Long style

Ovary

Nectar secreted
around the base
of ovary

Receptacle

b)

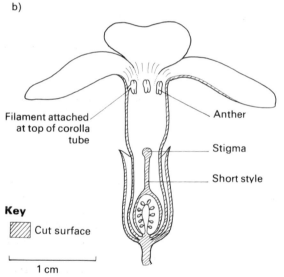

Filament attached
at top of corolla
tube

Anther

Stigma

Short style

Key

⊘ Cut surface

1 cm

Figure 3.13 Vertical section of a primrose (*Primula vulgaris*):
a) pin-eyed flowers, b) thrum-eyed flowers. The primrose flower
is an example of heterostyly, i.e. insects collecting nectar pick up
pollen on different parts of their bodies. They take pollen from
the anthers of flower a) to the stigma of flower b), and vice versa

dog's mercury and holly; most people are aware
that berries are found on some, but not all, holly
trees. There are other oddities; ground ivy has one
type of flower which is bisexual with both anthers
and carpels, and another type with carpels only.
Horse-chestnut has separate flowers, with either
anthers or carpels, in the same inflorescence.

• Other plants show *self-sterility* which may be
either genetically determined (usually by more
than one gene) or produced as a result of secretion
of growth inhibitors by pollen grain, pollen tube or
stigma. Horticulturalists can overcome such problems by treating pollen with plant growth substances, or by removing the stigma and style that
produce the inhibitors, so that germination of the
pollen grain takes place directly in the carpel. Many
pear and apple trees have to be planted with a
complementary variety as a pollinator because
they are self-sterile. For example, Cox's Orange
Pippin is an excellent pollinator for other varieties
of apple but, being self-sterile, it needs the presence of other pollinating varieties.

• Some plants set seed without fertilisation
(*apogamy*). An example is bramble which sometimes cross-pollinates as well to produce a range of
microspecies.

■ **Formation of the seed and fruit**

After fertilisation, changes take place in the carpel.
The ovary grows bigger, the wall becomes the fruit
wall (*pericarp*) and the seeds ripen (Fig.3.18). *Auxins*
(plant growth substances) produced by the carpel
not only stimulate fruit development but also make
sure that the fruit stays on the plant to give 'fruit
set'. Only the other flower parts, petals, stamens
and sometimes sepals, are shed.

The seed finally matures as its water content
drops from the normal 90% in plant tissues to
about 10-15%. This means that, without water to
act as a medium, enzymes do not operate, metabolic activities stop and the seed becomes dormant.

Some plants can set fruit without fertilisation, a
phenomenon known as *parthenocarpy*. Examples
are pineapple, banana and seedless varieties of
oranges and grapes. Parthenocarpy can be induced by administering auxins, as is done commercially with seedless tomatoes and peppers, or
gibberellins, as in peach, apricot and cherry. If pear
blossom is damaged by frost, fruit can still be
obtained by spraying the trees with gibberellins.

As the fruit ripens, respiration increases with the
production of another plant growth substance,
ethene. This, together with abscisic acid, stimulates the formation of an abscission layer at the
base of the fruit stalk and the fruit is then shed in a
similar way to leaf fall (Fig.1.23).

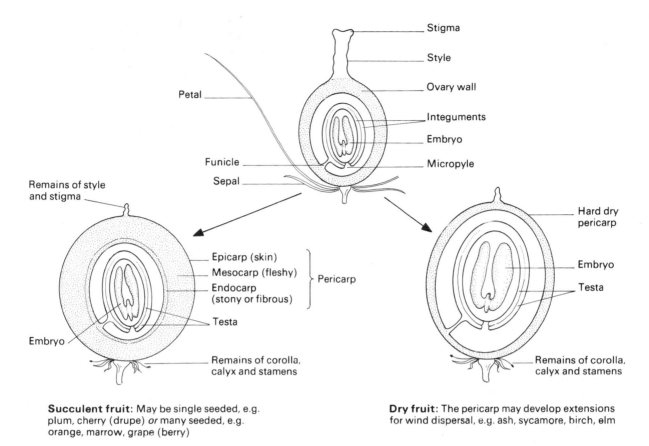

Figure 3.14 The development of a fruit

Below the central diagram, left side:

Succulent fruit: May be single seeded, e.g. plum, cherry (drupe) *or* many seeded, e.g. orange, marrow, grape (berry)

Below the central diagram, right side:

Dry fruit: The pericarp may develop extensions for wind dispersal, e.g. ash, sycamore, birch, elm

Q 1. What are the advantages to the grower of spraying plant growth substances to achieve fruit set?

2. Green tomatoes stored with a ripe apple ripen. Explain this.

■ THE CONTROL OF GERMINATION

An outline of the stages of germination has been described for the broad bean in Chapter 2. You will need to check which species is required in your particular examination syllabus. Ideally, you should grow your own seeds and observe their development and we have included annotated drawings of the germination of the sunflower (Fig.3.15) and barley to help you (Fig.3.16). The barley grain is referred to here because the processes going on in the seed have been studied in detail, mainly by biologists and biochemists in the brewing industry.

Conditions required for the germination of a mature seed are water, an optimum temperature, oxygen and the presence of plant growth substances. Research has shown that both types of plant growth substances - cytokinins and gibberellins - can break dormancy in some seeds. Little is known of the activity of cytokinins but they may be concerned with *t-RNA* synthesis (resulting in the manufacture of proteins). Used commercially, these substances have the effect of delaying the senescence of cabbage and lettuce leaves and keeping flowers fresh.

---

t-RNA transfer RNA is a molecule that carries amino acid molecules to the ribosomes in the cytoplasm. The amino acids are then joined together in long chains to produce different proteins

---

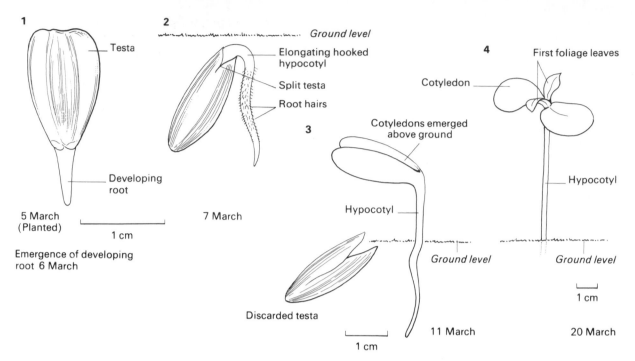

1

Testa

Developing root

5 March (Planted)

├─── 1 cm ───┤

Emergence of developing root 6 March

2

Ground level

Elongating hooked hypocotyl

Split testa

Root hairs

7 March

3

Cotyledons emerged above ground

Hypocotyl

Discarded testa

├─── 1 cm ───┤

11 March

4

First foliage leaves

Cotyledon

Hypocotyl

Ground level   Ground level

├─ 1 cm ─┤

20 March

Figure 3.15 Epigeal germination of sunflower (*Helianthus annuus*)

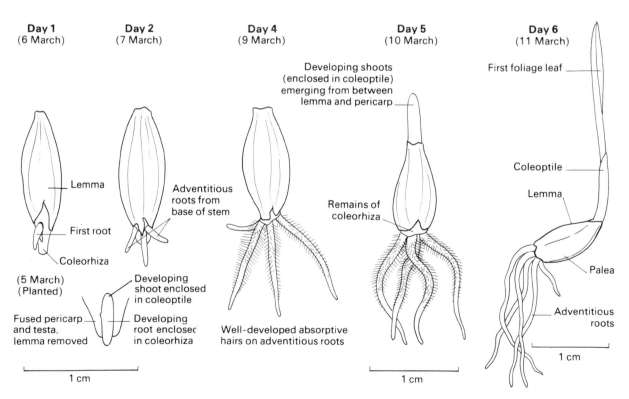

Day 1
(6 March)

Day 2
(7 March)

Day 4
(9 March)

Day 5
(10 March)

Day 6
(11 March)

Developing shoots (enclosed in coleoptile) emerging from between lemma and pericarp

First foliage leaf

Lemma

First root

Coleorhiza

(5 March)
(Planted)

Fused pericarp and testa, lemma removed

Developing shoot enclosed in coleoptile

Developing root enclosed in coleorhiza

Adventitious roots from base of stem

Well-developed absorptive hairs on adventitious roots

Remains of coleorhiza

Coleoptile

Lemma

Palea

Adventitious roots

├─── 1 cm ───┤   ├─── 1 cm ───┤   ├─── 1 cm ───┤

Figure 3.16 Stages in the epigeal germination of the barley grain (*Hordeum* sp.)

52

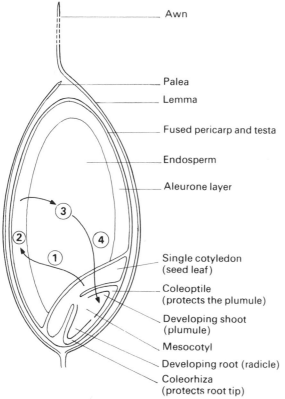

- Awn
- Palea
- Lemma
- Fused pericarp and testa
- Endosperm
- Aleurone layer
- Single cotyledon (seed leaf)
- Coleoptile (protects the plumule)
- Developing shoot (plumule)
- Mesocotyl
- Developing root (radicle)
- Coleorhiza (protects root tip)

(1) Gibberellin synthesis in cotyledon after water imbibition

(2) Gibberellin in aleurone layer stimulates formation of amylase from protein

(3) Amylase catalyses the breakdown of starch to maltose (then maltase continues the breakdown of maltose to glucose) in the endosperm

(4) Breakdown products move into the developing embryo for energy production and growth

Figure 3.17 Vertical section of a barley grain to show its structure and the mobilisation of its food stores

A study of barley (Fig.3.17) shows that gibberellin is synthesised after imbibition and diffuses to the aleurone layer where it stimulates the formation of the enzyme amylase from stored protein. The amylase moves into the endosperm and hydrolyses the breakdown of starch to maltose and maltase then continues the breakdown to glucose. Water is used to transport the soluble products of **hydrolysis** into the developing embryo. Initially these are used for respiration, providing energy for growth. With the release of carbon dioxide there is a net loss in dry mass of the seed during the initial

stages, and not until green leaves appear will the seedling make its own food and increase its mass, i.e. grow. Once the foliage leaves reach light, **photomorphogenesis** ensures the expansion of leaves, the development of chloroplasts for photosynthesis, development of strengthening xylem and phloem and a decrease in the rate of the growth of the shoot, producing a sturdy, stocky green plant.

 Compare germination in a dicotyledon with germination in a monocotyledon.

■ Malting barley

The malting of barley for brewing consists of several stages:

• Barley is steeped in water to allow imbibition, then removed and subjected to warm air for a few days before being very slowly dried. The drying stops metabolism at a stage when the enzymes, amylase and peptidase, have been activated (Fig.3.17 - day 1).

• The grains are then ground, mixed with a mash of starchy materials in water at 50-60°C and allowed to stand for about an hour. In this time, the amylase hydrolyses the starch to maltose and dextrins. Yeast is added and the yeast enzyme maltase breaks down maltose to glucose. After adding the yeast, the mix is kept at 30-35°C for several days.

• *Zymase* (a collection of about fourteen enzymes) in the yeast ferments the glucose to alcohol, the mixture producing bubbles of carbon dioxide. The resulting ethanol is the basis of whisky and beer.

---

hydrolysis the splitting of molecules by water. This enzyme action is similar to the splitting of starch by salivary amylase in the digestion of food

photomorphogenesis 'photo' meaning light, 'morphe' meaning form, and 'genesis' meaning birth

---

Answers to question on page 43.

Top = Insect pollinated
Middle = Wind pollinated
Bottom = Insect pollinated
(Note: some Advanced Level syllabuses require knowledge of the characteristics of certain families. These are to be found in Appendix 1.)

The chapter started with a mention of the 'dominant ferns' in the flora of 400 million years ago. It ends with a life cycle diagram of a fern. Note carefully the points where fertilisation and meiosis occur (Fig.3.18).

Q Compare this two-stage cycle with that of a flowering plant (Fig.3.6).

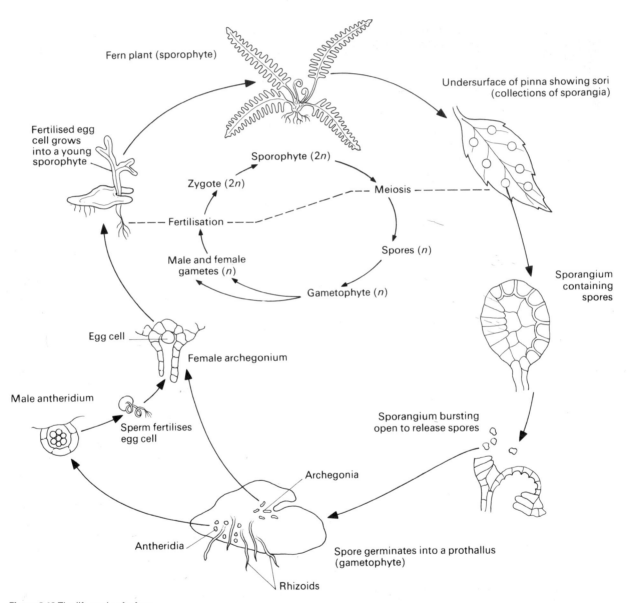

Figure 3.18 The life cycle of a fern

4 PLANTS FOR ALL SEASONS

Stem of green bananas (*Musa* sp.) covered with a plastic bag to protect the ripening fruit from pests

Growing bananas at the Arctic Circle seems impossible but the Icelandic hot springs heat the greenhouses where they produce the country's third most valuable export! We now have the science and technology to grow any plant wherever and whenever we wish.

We take it for granted that we can buy hyacinth and tulip bulbs in the autumn to flower in our homes at Christmas and that our gardens, with careful planning, can yield a succession of flowers throughout the year.

In the countryside, a seasonal succession is a basis for survival. Spring flowers, such as snowdrops, appear before leaves appear on the trees, making the maximum use of the light available. The appearance of snowdrops is soon followed by others, primroses, bluebells and the wind-pollinated catkins of hazel trees. In high summer we can find field scabious and meadowsweet in our meadows, and flowers of many umbellifers (for example, angelica) and composites in hedges and on roadside verges. There are local variations: the same range of plants cannot be grown in both Cornwall and the north of Scotland.

Q Try to find out how the modes of life of the snowdrop, primrose, hazel and angelica ensure their survival.

It is easy to accept these facts without question but the consideration of our temperate climate gives us some answers. Both temperature and day length gradually increase during spring and summer and then decrease through autumn and winter. In addition, rainfall varies throughout the year in different parts of Britain. The response to such environmental factors is a result of the activity of the plant growth substances mentioned in earlier chapters.

■ DORMANCY

Dormancy is a period when the plant has a very low metabolic rate and growth is at a standstill. Growth resumes only when the conditions necessary for normal activity prevail. Dormancy can affect the whole plant or just parts of it, such as buds and seeds, enabling the plant to survive periods of unfavourable climatic conditions. Annuals produce dormant seeds. In biennials (which take two years to mature and produce seed) and perennials (which flower every year), the shoots may die back while the overwintering structures (e.g. bulbs and tubers) become dormant. Larger perennials, like trees and shrubs, keep their shoots through the winter but leaves may fall, leaving dormant buds.

Because the factors affecting the breaking of dormancy and the onset of flowering are interdependent, we need to introduce some useful terms here:
• *Stratification* is the necessary exposure of seeds to a cold period, after imbibing water, to break dormancy (e.g. dog-rose and other members of the Rosaceae, cowslip, cereals, and trees such as pine).
• *Vernalisation* is the exposure of plants to a cold period in order to stimulate flowering (e.g. foxglove, honesty and primrose).
• *Photoperiodism* is the appropriate combination of light and dark periods which makes plants start to flower.

The breaking of dormancy and the resumption of growth may be triggered by changes in a number of factors such as light, temperature, and the relative amounts of growth substances (promoters and inhibitors).

■ LIGHT

In trees of temperate regions, such as birch, sycamore and beech, bud formation takes place in the autumn usually as a photoperiodic response to the shorter days. At this time, the level of abscisic acid (ABA) rises, it moves to the meristems and inhibits cell division and growth. The effect of light on dormancy in seeds is variable. In some, such as lettuce, it may be broken by light after water uptake; in other species, such as love-in-a-mist, germination is inhibited by light.

When it comes to the importance of light to the onset of flowering, plants can be divided into three groups.

■ Long-day (LD) plants

These are typical of a temperate climate, and require a 'long day' and short night before they start to flower. By long-day we mean *more* than ten hours of daylight in a 24 hour cycle (e.g. radish, spinach, larkspur and foxglove). Many of these also require vernalisation. It is interesting that plants in this group often have a compact rosette habit during their dormancy and then produce a flowering stalk with long internodes in summer.

Rosette of large-flowered evening primrose (*Oenothera erythrosepala*)

Leafy stalk of large-flowered evening primrose

■ Short-day (SD) plants

These will start to flower only when the daylight exposure is *less* than a critical length, varying considerably among species. Typically these plants originate nearer the equator than LD plants. In temperate climates, SD plants flower in late autumn, winter or early spring (e.g. chrysanthemum, pointsettia, Christmas cactus and cocklebur.

Pointsettia (*Euphorbia pulcherrima*)

■ Day-neutral (DN) plants

These are indifferent to the length of day. This group includes maize, cotton, cucumber and tomato.

Of the SD and LD plants, some have an absolute need for that particular day length (category A in Table 4.1), others (category B) will flower more quickly with the correct day length but will eventually flower even if the day length is not right.

A Long-day species with an absolute or qualitative LD requirement

Carnation (*Dianthus superbus*)
Sedum (*Sedum spectabile*)
Clover (*Trifolium* sp.)
Meadow fescue (*Festuca pratensis*)
Oat (*Avena sativa*)
Radish (*Raphanus sativa*)
Spinach (*Spinacea oleracea*)

B Long-day species with a quantitative LD requirement

Petunia (*Fetunia hybrida*)
Snapdragon (*Antirrhinum majus*)
Evening primrose (*Oenothera* sp.)
Garden pea (*Pisum sativum*)
Lettuce (*Lactuca sativa*)
Spring wheat (*Triticum aestivum*)
Turnip (*Brassica rapa*)

A Short-day species with an absolute or qualitative SD requirement

Chrysanthemum (*Chrysanthemum morfolium*)
Cocklebur (*Xanthium strumarium*)
Kalanchoe (*Kalanchoe blossfeldiana*)
Pointsettia (*Euphorbia pulcherrima*)
Strawberry (*Fragaria* sp.)
Soya bean (*Glycine max*)
Tobacco (*Nicotiana tobacum*)

B Short-day species with a quantitative SD requirement

Salvia (*Salvia splendens*)
Rice (*Oryza sativa*)
Sugar cane (*Saccharum officinarum*)

C Day-neutral species (DN)

Holly (*Ilex aquifolium*)
Cucumber (*Cucumis sativus*)
Cotton - one variety (*Gossypium hirsutum*)
Maize (*Zea mays*)

(Data for categories A and B adapted from Wareing and Phillips, *The control of growth and differentiation in plants*. Data for category C was adapted from Salisbury, *Plant Physiology*.)

Table 4.1 Some examples of long-day and short-day plants

Investigations by Hamner and Bonner in 1938 revealed that the term *photoperiodism* is a misnomer because in all plants, it is not the total intensity of light received but the actual length of the *dark period* that is important (Fig.4.1). With an SD plant, even a flash of light interrupting its period of darkness can inhibit flowering. This applies even to artificial light - so be careful which cupboard you use for your Christmas bulbs. (The kalanchoe which lives in our sitting room has never flowered; perhaps a reflection on the LD habits of its owners!)

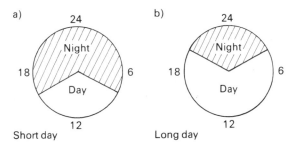

Figure 4.1 The pattern of day and night during a 24 hour cycle of: a) a short-day (SD) plant, b) a long-day (LD) plant (shown here as a 9 hour and a 15 hour day respectively)

Day length varies considerably as we travel from the equator to the poles. Also seasonal changes become more extreme nearer the poles. For example, summer day length in the north of Scotland is several hours longer than in the south of England and the opposite occurs in winter.

■ CASE HISTORY

Pointsettia is an SD plant. Many of us have a poinsettia plant at Christmas and the bright red bracts are attractive. However the following year, the plant, if it has survived, has grown leggy and the bracts remain obstinately green. The secret of the horticulturist is in deceiving the plant into 'thinking' that Christmas is the right time to produce the beautiful, coloured bracts. Starting in September and for a period of eight or nine weeks, pointsettia requires no more than ten hours of light a day, so it should be transferred to a dark cupboard to avoid receiving more than this. Unfortunately, the plant's original compact size cannot be regained since this was achieved by a chemical dwarfing technique.

 Write a suitable Garden Shop label giving instructions for the care of a pointsettia plant.

■ RECEPTION OF THE PHOTOPERIODIC STIMULUS

In the 1930s, a Russian scientist, Chailachjan, demonstrated that it is the leaves and not the shoot apex that respond to light conditions prior to flowering. He concluded that some chemical 'signal', which he called *florigen*, was transmitted from the leaves. Hamner and Bonner discovered that in cocklebur also, the centre of response was the leaf. Cocklebur is a useful experimental plant as it can be made to flower just two weeks after light and dark treatment. A plant with all its leaves removed will not respond to the photoperiod but one with just one eighth of a fully expanded leaf will.

There has been no success in isolating Chailachjan's hypothetical florigen. However, flowering may be induced in some species by *gibberellins*, a large group of plant growth substances of which gibberellic acid (GA_3) is one. Gibberellins and auxins act *synergistically*, that is, the effect of these substances acting together is greater than the sum of their individual effects in other words AB > A + B. In the pineapple, flowering can be induced by ethene and auxin. In some species such as strawberry and currant, both SD plants, flowering can be promoted by naturally-occurring abscisic acid (ABA) but, conversely, this plant growth substance will inhibit flowering in the LD rye-grass. GA_3 does not induce flowering in some species requiring vernalisation, although GA_4 and GA_7 (other forms of gibberellic acid) will do so in alpine forget-me-not. In addition, some SD and LD plants cannot be induced to flower following treatment with any combination of known naturally–occurring plant growth substances.

Genetic studies may prove helpful in sorting out these apparent contradictions. It is known that in campion there are separate genes for stem growth (internode elongation) and flowering. In rye, a single gene controls the difference between spring and winter forms.

■ The photoperiodic response

The blue pigment *phytochrome* was first isolated by means of a spectrophotometer in 1959. It is a molecule consisting of a light-absorbing pigment, *phycobilin*, plus a protein portion. We now know that the photoperiodic response is due to very small amounts of phytochrome (too small for us to see the colour) which, although distributed throughout the plant, is found in the greatest concentration in the growing tips of the shoot. This pigment *reversibly changes colour* when exposed to red (660 nm) or far red (730 nm) light. The two colour variations are known as P660 or P_R (absorbing red light) and P730 or P_{FR} (absorbing far red light). There is a rapid change of P660 to P730 when phytochrome absorbs red light and P730 to P660 when it absorbs far red light. The former reaction predominates in daylight, as sunlight contains more red than far red light, so P730 tends to accumulate. In the dark there is a slow conversion of P730 to P660 without exposure to far red light, although this has only been shown in dicotyledons (Fig.4.2). P730 is the active form of phytochrome and may initiate enzyme action and stimulate or inhibit growth, depending on the species; P660 is the inactive form.

Far red light produces the type of growth seen in *etiolation* (i.e. plants grown in the dark with long internodes and small, yellow leaves). In contrast,

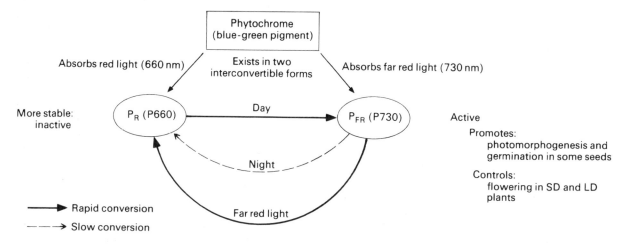

Figure 4.2 The interconversion of the two forms of phytochrome, PR and PFR

normal leaf expansion is stimulated by red light. Red light promotes flowering in LD plants and inhibits it in SD plants. Because the conversion from P730 to P660 in the dark is slow, only long nights give enough time for removal of enough P730 in SD plants to permit flowering. GA_3 promotes flowering in some LD plants, especially rosette plants, and inhibits it in some SD plants, thus mimicking the effect of red light. What we do not know is whether P730 stimulates the production of gibberellins, and whether it is, therefore, a plant growth substance which promotes flowering. Could it possibly be the elusive florigen?

Q 1. Using the above information, explain in terms of phytochrome activity a) the result of Hamner and Bonner's work on cocklebur and b) why some varieties of lettuce seeds will only germinate if exposed briefly to light.

2. Devise an experiment to determine the effects of treating a LD plant, such as oat seedlings, with GA_3.

■ THE SEASONAL EFFECTS OF TEMPERATURE

Temperature is important in determining when biennials and perennials flower. Biennials (e.g. cabbage, foxglove and honesty) which remain vegetative during the first season's growth, need the cold of their first winter to promote flowering the following year. These plants can remain vegetative for a number of years if kept in a warm greenhouse which prevents vernalisation. Perennials normally produce flowers each year, but some (e.g. primrose, violet and wallflower) require vernalisation.

Gassner in 1918 first recognised the importance of temperature in his work on the flowering of cereals, such as wheat and rye, and their winter and spring varieties (Chapter 5). A temperature of about 4°C for a period of four days to three months, depending on the species, is the optimum cold exposure.

Melchers and Lang in the 1960s found that the vernalisation stimulus can be passed from one plant to another by grafting. They supposed a plant growth substance might be formed as a result of the chilling and called it *vernalin*. However, as the addition of GA can induce flowering in place of vernalisation, it may be that vernalin is a GA.

Compare this with the breaking of dormancy in seeds during stratification which is associated with increased GA activity and usually a reduction in growth inhibitors. There seems to be no clear pattern of response among species. For example, the SD chrysanthemum, LD cabbage and DN ragwort all require vernalisation to stimulate flowering.

■ GROWTH INHIBITORS

In many fruits and seeds there are naturally occurring chemicals that behave as growth inhibitors, although their mode of action is unclear. For example, ABA is one in ash seeds. An increase in GA may cancel out the effect of the ABA (an example of *antagonism*). Soaking seeds in water, making the testa more permeable, may also leach out some of the inhibitors.

INVESTIGATION

It is suggested that inhibitors are present in the flesh of tomatoes. Devise (and if possible carry out) an experiment to test whether washing fresh tomato seeds increases the rate of seed germination. You could also try to test ash seeds in a similar way.

■ PERMEABILITY OF THE TESTA

Seeds with a tough or woody testa can be made to germinate by scratching them with sandpaper or giving them a prolonged soak in water. Even date 'stones' will germinate successfully if they are soaked first. They become slimy as the decomposing action of microorganisms softens the stone, imitating natural events. Some people see a challenge in getting all sorts of exotic seeds to germinate - orange, avocado and even coffee (only try with unroasted beans!).

To summarise, the mechanisms by which light and temperature affect dormancy and the interactions of all the factors involved is by no means clear. We must assume that:
• it is unlikely that there are just single flowering and vernalisation plant growth substances operating in all species.
• there are interactions between plant growth substances and environmental factors, including light and temperature, that may be highly species specific.
• further study is required to determine patterns of interaction. Modern plant science addresses these problems and studies of crop plants are vital for the survival of human populations.

■ TROPISMS

Can we use any of this information in deciding the best place for different species of house plant to grow, whether it be summer or winter? A plant has to respond to light because light is essential for food production. It does this by a positive growth movement towards light (*phototropism*). *Geotropism* is the response to gravity. The developing shoot and root of a seed planted upside-down turn and grow in the right direction.

It was Charles Darwin's experiments on phototropism that began the process of the discovery of auxins. He, and later workers (Boysen-Jensen in 1913, followed by Went in 1929), used oat seedlings for their experiments. Because the young shoots emerge enclosed in a sheath (coleoptile), the tip remains straight as it pushes through the soil, so any bending movements due to an external stimulus can easily be seen. This straight tip is convenient as it can be covered with tiny foil caps, or decapitated and little agar (jelly) blocks balanced on the cut surface (see Fig.4.3). If you try to repeat any of these experiments, you will realise the skill required - the coleoptiles are very small!

Q 1. Study the diagrams in Fig.4.3a and state what Darwin could have concluded.

2. Boysen-Jensen used a thin mica plate inserted horizontally across the coleoptile below its tip. His results are shown in Fig.4.3b. What conclusions can you draw from Boysen-Jensen's experiments?

3. Went took these experiments a stage further. He cut the tips off normal coleoptiles and placed each on a small agar block. He then transferred the agar blocks to the tips of decapitated coleoptiles. He did a similar exercise using untreated agar blocks for comparison (as a control). His results are shown in Fig.4.3c. What conclusions can you draw from Went's experiments?

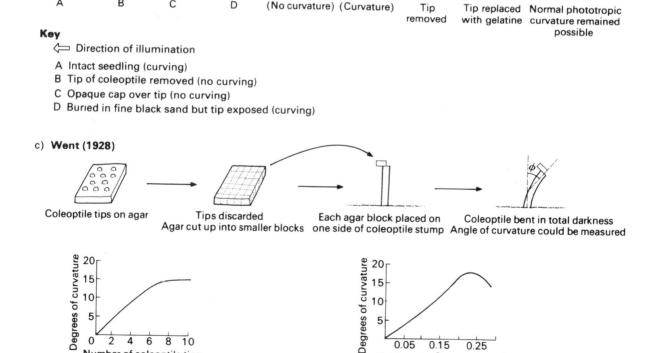

Figure 4.3 A summary of experiments by: a) Darwin, b) Boysen-Jensen and c) Went, to demonstrate the existence of auxins in plants

Went found that the degree of bending was directly proportional to the amount of auxin present. This is the basis of a bioassay; measuring the effect of a substance to determine how much of the substance is present.

As a result of all these experiments, we can assume that a plant growth substance (auxin) moves laterally away from light in the zone of elongation of the coleoptile tip and then moves downwards where it is broken down by enzymes. Where there is the greater concentration of auxin, the cells are stimulated to grow, resulting in a bending towards the light (Fig.4.4).

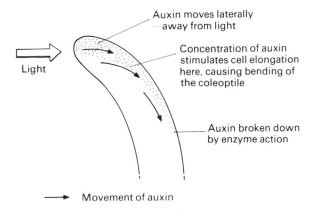

Movement of auxin

Figure 4.4 How light may cause the movement of auxin from its site of synthesis in a coleoptile tip

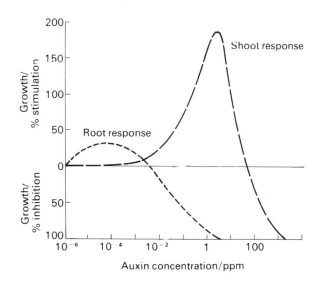

Figure 4.5 The effect of auxin concentration on the growth of shoots and roots

Auxin is made in the tips of shoots and in young leaves (some may be made in the roots). Transport from cell to cell is by diffusion with long-distance transport in the phloem. The effect of the auxin concentration is different in shoots and roots. Lower concentrations of auxin stimulate growth in roots, higher concentrations stimulate shoot and inhibit root growth (Fig.4.5).

Q Why do pot plants on a window–sill need to be turned daily? Apart from a bending of the stem, do other movements occur? How does the plant benefit from the response?

Mature plants, in an absence of red light, become *etiolated*. This can be useful in getting early crops with tender growth. Gardeners 'force' rhubarb and chicory by keeping the plants in the dark. Bean sprouts are produced by forcing mung bean seeds. To get a sturdy, stocky house plant, however, the correct amount of light is needed to retard elongation. Some plants that live in naturally shady places (e.g. some ferns), cannot survive in sunlight on a window–sill. The diffuse light and humid atmosphere of a bathroom is more appropriate.

Etiolation in a mung bean

The potted chrysanthemum plant bought from the florist is a compact mass of flowering shoots. To achieve this form, use is made of the way buds behave. The *apical (terminal) bud* is said to be *dominant* because its growth inhibits that of lateral buds. This *apical dominance* results in a long main stem and few side branches (Fig.4.6). To produce the maximum numbers of flowers, therefore, the

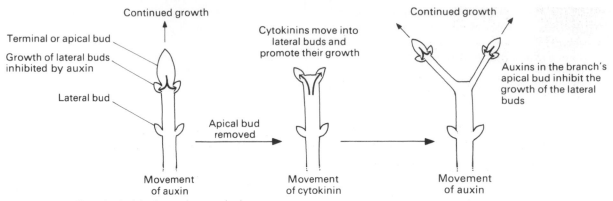

Figure 4.6 The effect of apical dominance in a woody shoot

terminal bud is removed, allowing the development of lateral buds and producing a bushy plant. Although we do not know how auxins exert their influence, it appears that the removal of the terminal bud inactivates the high levels of ABA in the lateral buds, while cytokinin together with auxin breaks their dormancy. It is possible that cytokinins, made in the roots and transported in the xylem, move to where auxins are manufactured in the shoots and act synergistically with them.

The pruning of fruit trees makes use of the same principle, encouraging the development of many flower-producing side shoots and increasing the crop. Apple trees can be 'trained' as *cordons*, a single trunk with many short side branches, maximising the number of trees and the size of the crop in the minimum of space.

It does not matter which way up seeds are planted because roots are positively geotropic, so will always grow downwards. Again, the removal of the root tip prevents this response. This can be demonstrated in a similar way to phototropism. As with all experiments, a control is necessary and a device to make gravity act for equal times on all sides of the plant and hence cancelling its effect. Such a device is a *clinostat*. This is an electrically-driven circular plate, which, when rotating at about four

revolutions per hour, effectively removes the one-sided effect of gravity and the roots continue to grow in their original direction. In geotropism, the auxin in the root tip becomes more concentrated on the lower side, inhibiting growth there and so, as the upper side grows more rapidly, the root grows downwards (Fig.4.7).

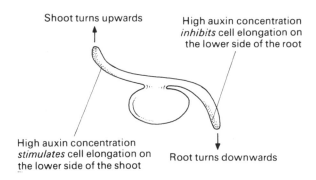

Figure 4.7 Auxin distribution in a horizontally–growing seedling and why it does not matter if seeds are planted the wrong way up

■ ECONOMIC IMPORTANCE OF PLANTS IN AND OUT OF SEASON

We like to make use of the variety of fruits and vegetables we can buy out of season. We can grow herbs on the kitchen window–sill or flowers for decoration, using the warmth of centrally heated homes or greenhouses and artificial light.

Before the advance of technology, we had to rely on the transport of more exotic species from their country of origin as they came into season. Now, even during 'unnatural' times of the year, the horticulturist can use complex treatments, both natural and chemical, to provide the plants the public asks for and to make a profit. The garden centre is now big business!

Clinostat

OUR DAILY BREAD

CHAPTER 5

Global granary in peril as rains desert America

The world's reserves of grain are perilously low this year as a result of continuing drought in the US. Meanwhile, the White House is showing signs of anger with government scientists who claim that the American climate could be changing as part of the greenhouse effect.

The produce from American farms usually makes up around 40 per cent of the grain traded on world markets. But American reserves are down to 550 million bushels, half the stockpile at the end of 1988. This figure represents only 20 per cent of annual demand in the US for grain for domestic use and export, which is the second lowest figure since 1945.

This year's dry weather succeeds last year's drought and several recent dry years, bringing concern that the country may be experiencing a shift in climate of the kind predicted by several climatic models as likely in the early stages of global warming due to the greenhouse effect. California is in its third year of drought, a phenomenon that has not happened for 400 years.

New Scientist 3 June 1989

Figure 5.1

 1. Why is North America named as the global granary?

2. What evidence is given for the claim that the North American climate is changing?

3. What is the greenhouse effect?

■ THE ECONOMIC IMPORTANCE OF THE GRAMINEAE (GRASS FAMILY)

There are 8000 plant species in 600 genera in the family Gramineae. They make up a quarter of the world's vegetation cover, with about 12 species being the staple diets of the human population (Table 5.1). Cultivated species include not only wheat, but also oats, barley, rye, maize (corn), rice, sugar cane and several genera and species of millet including sorghum and teff.

Cereal	Production / tonnes x 10^6
Wheat	515
Rice	458
Maize	452
Barley	182
Sorghum	62
Oats	48
Rye	32
Millet	28
Others (estimate)	11
Total	1788

Table 5.1 World production of cereals

Country	Production / tonnes x 10^6
China	87.0
Soviet Union	84.5
USA	56.8
India	45.2
France	26.8
Canada	26.1
Turkey	18.8
Australia	12.1
UK	12.0
Pakistan	11.9
Spain	5.5
Italy	4.9
World Total	515.0
EC total	65.4

Table 5.2 Annual wheat production in the major wheat–producing countries

Wheat is the staple food crop that grows in temperate climates or at higher altitude in hotter areas. In wet tropical climates, rice is the staple food. In dry tropical climates, it is maize.

Archaeologists have uncovered the remains of human food stores and these give us information about the development of cereals as staple foods. The early agriculturalists must have learned to save the best seed and breed it to produce higher-yielding varieties. This is illustrated by finds of fossil corn from Mexico from 5000 BC.

There are many modern varieties used for producing cornflour, hard grains for popcorn, and sweet corn with high sugar levels.

Rice (Fig.5.2a) originated in Asia and was a staple food in China as early as 2800 BC. It is now grown from the equator to as far north as Japan, in South America and Africa, North America and Australia. Rice may be grown either in water (paddy rice) or, to a lesser extent, on dry land (upland rice). It can either be ground into flour or used as the grain, boiled or fried, or fermented into rice wine (sake). Rice contains a lower proportion of protein than wheat.

Millet species are drought resistant, tolerate poor soils and most can be stored for as long as five years as unthreshed ears. They tend to be grown in poor areas, on the margins of deserts, which results in low yield. Most millets have a higher level of minerals than other cereals, especially finger millet. Most millet is ground into meal for use. Sorghum may also be used as animal feed or made into beer.

Sugar cane (Fig.5.2b) provides more than half the world's sugar and is grown mainly in the tropics.

The stems are crushed to extract the sucrose. Modern varieties can produce more human food per hectare than any other crop but sugar cane rapidly reduces the amount of nutrients in the soil so it needs a well-fertilised soil and plenty of water to maintain a good yield.

Rye (Fig.5.2c) is grown in the colder parts of Europe and Russia and has a grain similar in composition to wheat. It is used for making black bread, crispbreads and whisky. The straw is useful for thatching, paper making and straw hats.

Oats (Fig.5.2d) can also tolerate a colder climate than wheat and are traditionally grown in Scotland. Not only are they especially important for their dietary fibre, but they are also used as animal feed and as a source of furfural, and its derivatives, used in oil refining, and in the manufacture of nylon, antiseptics and synthetic rubber.

Barley (Fig.5.2e) was the dominant cereal in Europe in the Neolithic and Bronze ages. Nowadays most British barley is used for malting in the brewing industry. Some is used as pearl barley. Low quality grains are used as animal feed.

The majority of plants in the family Gramineae are the grasses and these plants are of utmost importance in the feeding of both domesticated livestock (hay and silage) and wild herbivores. In Britain, many high-yielding, rapid growing varieties (e.g. Italian rye-grass, cock's-foot, timothy and rough-stalked meadow-grass) are seeded on to ploughed land to improve pasture. Grasses can cope with continual grazing because their growing points are at the base of the plant, not at the tips of the shoots as in dicotyledons. Different species and varieties of grasses are used on sportsfields for

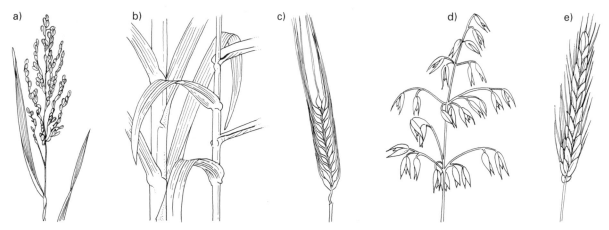

Figure 5.2 a) Rice plant (*Oryza sativa*), b) Sugar cane plant (*Saccharum officinarum*), c) Rye (*Secale cereale*), d) Oats (*Avena sativa*), e) Barley (*Hordeum* sp.)

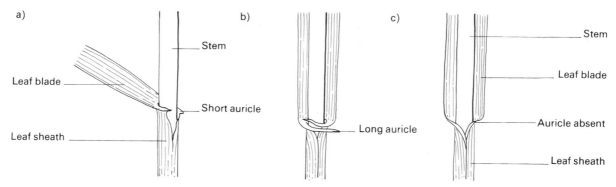

Figure 5.3 Can you identify a cereal crop before it flowers? The junction of the leaf blade and sheath of: a) wheat, b) barley, c) oats to show their recognition features

specialist playing surfaces. The requirements of Cardiff Arms Park would not be the same as those for Wimbledon!

■ GENETICS OF WHEAT

Wheat species fall into three groups:

Group 1   14 chromosomes in the diploid number i.e. $2n = 14$, $n = 7$
Group 2   28 chromosomes (tetraploid) i.e. $4n = 4 \times 7$
Group 3   42 chromosomes (hexaploid) i.e. $6n = 6 \times 7$

The $2n=14$ plants are the basic plants. The $4n$ plants have arisen as hybrids of $2n$ wheats crossed with other diploid grasses. The $6n$ plants have arisen as hybrids of $4n$ wheats crossed with other diploid grasses.

The three sets of chromosomes are denoted A, B and C for the diploid, tetraploid and hexaploid plants respectively.

The $2n$ wheats are the most ancient of the wheat species and examples are *Triticum boeoticum* and *T. monococcum* (Einkhorn).

One example of a $4n$ wheat is *T. dicoccum* (Emmer), recovered from Egyptian tombs 2500 BC. A modern example is *T. durum* (pasta wheat) grown mainly in the USA, Italy and Spain.

The $6n$ wheats are subspecies of *T. aestivum*, the most recently evolved bread wheat (Fig.5.4).

The diploid grasses involved in the crosses to produce hybrids are *Aegilops* spp.

Modern wheat is derived from primitive wheat, itself a cross between two grasses - *Triticum boeoticum* and *Aegilops speltoides*. It originated in Asia Minor and has since been developed as one of the staple foods of Western civilisations.

In Britain, with its temperate, seasonal climate, two types of wheat are grown.
• *Spring wheat* is sown in early spring and is harvested in the autumn of the same year.
• *Winter wheat* is sown in late autumn and is harvested the following autumn. The difference between these two types is caused by a single gene.

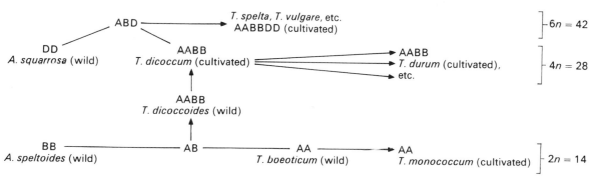

Figure 5.4 The history of diploid, tetraploid and hexaploid wheats

In order to mature, wheat needs 750 mm annual rainfall and a certain number of days when the temperature is above 5°C. Below this, enzyme reactions are too slow for growth and development.

In Canada, with its very severe winters, winter wheat cannot survive so spring varieties have to be grown. In climates where both can grow, winter wheat produces the greater yield. In Britain, most wheat is grown in the south; in parts of the north it is too wet and there is not enough sunshine to ripen the crop.

■ GERMINATION OF WHEAT

Wheat germinates like other grasses (Fig.5.5). The developing root emerges first but, unlike the broad bean, it is protected by the *coleorhiza* (root sheath) through which it soon bursts. The developing shoot then emerges protected by the *coleoptile* (plumage sheath). Also, unlike the bean, the stem nodes produce a fibrous root system extending 150 cm deep into the soil and branches (*tillers*) grow from the base of the leaves inside the stem and not from the shoot tip (Fig.5.6). Eventually flowers arise at the tips of the shoots.

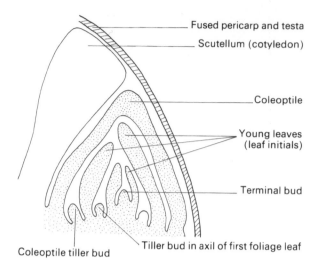

Figure 5.6 Section through part of a wheat grain to show the shoot area of the embryo and the tiller buds. The wheat embryo already contains the axillary buds which will grow out into branch stems known as tillers

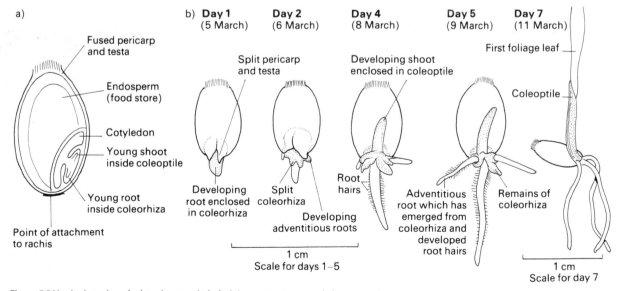

Figure 5.5 Vertical section of: a) a wheat grain (a fruit known as a caryopsis because of the fused pericarp and testa), b) stages in the germination of the wheat grain

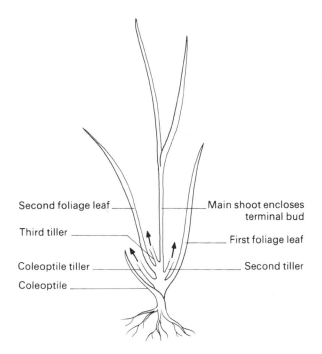

Figure 5.7 A seedling showing the origin of the tillers from axillary tiller buds. Internodes between tillers are very short. Each tiller grows roots at the nodes and produces a flower head (ear). Tillers form at the soil surface or not more than 2.5 cm below the surface. Each tiller may also branch at the base to give a total of one to nine stems (culms) for each wheat plant

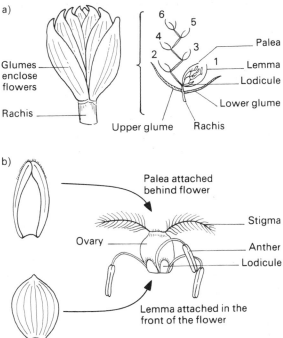

Figure 5.8 The structure of wheat flowers: a) one spikelet containing six flowers, b) the component parts of a single flower

INVESTIGATION

■ TESTING THE VIABILITY OF WHEAT

Before growing, it is essential that the quality of the grain is tested to ensure maximum yield.

The tetrazolium test

This gives a quick estimate of the viability of grain samples. This test depends on the fact that cells in a living (viable) grain will react with the reagent, because they are carrying out reduction (dehydrogenase) reactions, once the enzymes in the grain are provided with water as a solvent. The reagent is a dilute solution (0.1% to 1% with a pH between 6 and 7) of 2,3,5-triphenyl tetrazolium chloride or bromide in water.

To carry out the test:

• Take a sample of wheat grains. (A farmer would use four lots of 100 grains to get a representative replicated sample.)

• Soak the grains in water to soften the testa until they have finished imbibing water.

• Cut the grain in half lengthwise and immerse it in the colourless tetrazolium solution. (The solution is sensitive to light, keep it away from direct light.)

• Living grains will stain red where reduction reactions are taking place, in both the developing root and shoot. Dead or damaged tissues will not stain red. Calculate the percentage of viable grains in the sample.

Percentage germination test

Grow a sample of wheat grains and calculate the number that germinate as a percentage of the number in the original sample. Devise a suitable method for such a test and, if possible, carry it out. (This is a longer process, days instead of hours, so the chemical test has a great advantage.) If you can do both investigations, compare the results from the two tests.

The wheat flower

Wheat is a wind-pollinated grass, as are all the cereals (Fig.5.8). The 'ear' consists of a spike of flowers, which are monoecious i.e. they contain both stamens and carpels. The spike is divided into spikelets, each consisting of 5-9 flowers (some of which are sterile or have stamens only), producing up to five grains. Some wheats, have long awns (thread–like bristles), such as *Triticum durum*. *Triticum aestivum*, bread wheat grown in Britain, may or may not have awns. Cross-pollination normally occurs, although some cereals can self-pollinate as a result of their anthers dehiscing when the flower is still in bud.

Harvesting

In wild wheat, the central stalk of the spike, the rachis, shatters to distribute the single-seeded grains. Cultivated varieties are the result of artificial selection to produce a non-shatter rachis which can be harvested with the grain still in the ear. In the past in Britain, harvesting involved cutting and binding the wheat into sheaves; stooking or stacking the sheaves for drying; threshing to separate the grains and winnowing to separate the chaff. Nowadays, a combine harvester does all these jobs. The ripe wheat grain which leaves the combine harvester has to be dried at 65°C to a moisture content of 15%. At this level of moisture, sound grain can be kept in bulk if it is checked at intervals for insect infestation or increasing temperature in damper patches. For unventilated long-term storage, the moisture content must be 14% or lower.

 Why is it necessary to dry grain before storage?

The grain is stored in silos or weatherproof sheds; protected from rats, mice and other mammals and birds which would not only eat it, but also contaminate it with their faeces and urine.

WHEAT AS A FOOD

Variations in the way the grain is milled produces different types of flour; white or wholemeal. Milling breaks up the grains into their components; the pericarp and testa (bran) which is the dietary fibre, the aleurone layer, the embryo and the starchy endosperm. If the bran is mechanically separated from the endosperm (a process which removes some of the protein, leaving a larger proportion of starch), the resulting white flour has a lower food value. By retaining the embryo and the bran, we obtain wholemeal flour, containing more nutrients and fibre (see Table 5.3).

Food type	White (plain) flour/%	Stoneground (wholemeal) flour/%
Lipid	1.0	2.0
Protein	9.0	14.0
Carbohydrate	72.8	70.0
Fibre	3.0	9.6

Table 5.3 The composition of white and wholemeal flour

 What do you think makes up the rest of the 100% in both the flour types shown in Table 5.3?

	Western world	Developing world
Intake:		
Protein	12%	11%
Carbohydrate	48%	77%
Lipid	40%	12%
Fibre	15-20g per day	60-120g per day
Output: Faeces	80-120g per day	300-500g per day
Time for food to pass through gut:	70 hours	30 hours

Table 5.4 The differences in food intake, faecal output and the time it takes for food to pass through the gut in the western world compared with the developing world

 Diseases of the gut are far more common in the Western world. Could this be attributed to diet?

Most of the wheat we eat is in the form of bread. In making bread, we use a microorganism, a single-celled yeast (*Saccharomyces* sp.). First the yeast is mixed with some sugar and warm milk or water (why?) before it is added to the flour. The mixture is kneaded. The protein, gluten, in the flour makes dough sticky and elastic, trapping the carbon dioxide produced by the fermentation of the sugar by yeast. The dough is then proved, i.e. left to rise in a warm place, causing the carbon dioxide gas to expand and the dough to become spongy. The risen dough, when it is baked, sets with this spongy consistency. The heat of the oven, of course, kills the yeast cells and evaporates any ethanol that may have been formed by *anaerobic respiration* (alcoholic fermentation) as oxygen in the dough was used up.

Bread wheats are of two types. *Hard wheat* contains more gluten and gives a 'strong' flour with coarse, gritty grains good for making bread. It grows best in places with low rainfall and plenty of sun (e.g. North America). *Soft wheat* has less gluten and is used mainly for biscuits, confectionery and animal feed, although more is now used for bread in Britain especially if mixed with hard wheat flour. Soft wheat will grow in areas with a relatively high rainfall (e.g. Britain).

Hardness and strength are separate genetic characters but almost always occur together and so are probably linked on the same chromosome. Bread is low in lysine, an essential amino acid, so it is not suitable as a sole source of protein.

 Why are beans on toast a healthy combination? (Hint: look back at Chapter 2.)

■ CROP PRODUCTION

When we consider the cost of crop production, we need to compare the energy costs put into growing the crop with the value of the harvest. Farmers grow crops to earn a living and they can only do this if output (in terms of the value of the harvested crop) exceeds the input (the cost of land, labour, fertilisers and pesticides). If we analyse these costs, we find that they can be divided into two areas.
• *Fixed costs* which include regular labour, the cost of machinery and its maintenance, rent or business rates and the upkeep of buildings. These costs are present whether crops are grown or not.
• *Variable costs* which include cost of seed, fertiliser, pesticides, seasonal labour and fuel. These will vary with the volume of production and the type of crop grown.
Recently, there has been a trend towards intensive farming, with animals and with plant crops, bringing both advantages and disadvantages in terms of environmental effects. Extensive breeding programmes have produced higher yielding crops.

These are grown in bigger fields, achieved by grubbing out hedges, which can be worked with larger machines and fewer pairs of hands. Following higher crop and animal production rates within Europe as a whole, there has been some overproduction of crops. In some cases, this has resulted in 'quotas' to restrict either the type of crop grown or the amount of it. One problem in disposing of these 'surplus mountains' to more needy parts of the world, is that people have preferences for particular types of food based on their culture. Western foods can alter these p references with disastrous effects for the local cultivators. More recently, farmers in the EC have been paid to 'set aside' land; in other words, either to use it for some other non-agricultural commercial activity, e.g. leisure (which contributes to the farm's fixed costs), or simply not to grow crops. More positively, the 'set aside' grants could encourage farmers to manage small areas of uncultivated land such as woodland or meadows in the interest of conservation.

■ The advantages of intensive cultivation
A single crop grown in a field is known as a *monoculture*. There are some advantages in this.
• High yields can be obtained by using an appropriate variety, by providing a suitable environment and by using high levels of artificial fertilisers. For example, an average yield of winter wheat is 3.0-5.5 tons per hectare (plus nearly four tons of straw). For spring wheat the figures are slightly lower, 2.5-5.0 tons per hectare with about the same amount of straw.
• Lower labour costs are possible by using machines to plough, sow, spray and harvest, producing greater efficiency.
• A maximum yield for a minimum area of land can be achieved. Hedge removal leaves fewer 'dead corners', crop yield being lower on the edges of fields near hedges owing to shading and the uptake of nutrients by the hedge plants.

■ The disadvantages of intensive cultivation
• Varieties that produce high yields must be bred to suit the particular conditions of the area. Because they grow rapidly with nitrogen fertilisers, the stalks of cereals are weak and easily blown down so short-stalked varieties had to be developed. The breeding of new varieties can take a number of years and is expensive.

• Heavy machinery is not only expensive to maintain and fuel but it also compacts the ground and, over a number of years, will destroy the soil texture.

• Hedge removal to allow larger machines to operate removes corridors of habitat along which wildlife can move.

• Because there are many plants growing close together, a humid microclimate is generated in which pests and diseases spread rapidly. Excess use of pesticides may also damage the environment, polluting waterways and harming wildlife. The costs of insecticides and herbicides are high.

• The new high-yielding varieties of wheat, and other crops, require a large input of fertiliser compared with older strains. Artificial fertilisers and pesticides are costly to produce in terms of energy consumed.

■ Some long-term effects of intensive cultivation

Because the earth is laid bare between harvesting and the emergence of the new seedlings in a monoculture, wind and water erosion of topsoil occurs, with the loss of habitat for soil organisms important in the recycling of nutrients. This effect is worsened if hedges are removed. We are already seeing this effect in East Anglia and in Dust Bowl of North America. In New Zealand, Monterey pine is planted as a dense windbreak, 10 m tall, striding across the Canterbury Plains - a second use for a timber crop.

A monoculture with no hedges is unstable as an ecosystem. It is like an immature ecosystem; (e.g. one which has few species and so is susceptible to any changes in the physical environment). The monoculture could easily be totally destroyed by storm, drought or disease.

Excessive use of chemical pesticides and fertilisers over long periods of time leads to an imbalance and a reduction on the number of species in the food chains. Increasingly, water supplies and foods become contaminated, affecting both animals, feeding on the crop or drinking the water, and humans at the end of food chains. Pests become resistant to chemicals. Since 1950 pesticide-resistant smut and rust fungi and aphids have become more common. Fungus-resistant varieties of wheat are bred but new strains of fungi evolve to attack them. Huge areas of monoculture can be wiped out by rapid spread of a disease. The older grains had greater genetic diversity and a greater range of pest resistance. The crop was interspersed with weeds forming an alternative food source for pests.

Diseases, under those conditions, spread more slowly.

Machinery causes compaction in a soil lacking humus because of the use of chemical fertilisers.

All these problems tell us that cultivations methods will have to change in the future if the world is still to be fed and fed in an environmentally safe way.

■ The use of artificial fertilisers

Harvested crops deplete soil nutrients. These nutrients can be replaced by use of artificial fertilisers, use of organic waste materials, or growing a leguminious crop in a rotation.

Artificial fertilisers contain well-defined chemical compounds, such as nitrates and phosphates of potassium and ammonia, in contrast with organic fertilisers whose source is largely waste materials such as animal faeces, blood and bone meal from abattoirs, and plant compost. It is sensible to use a minimum quantity of artificial fertilisers to produce an optimum yield; above this level the increased yield is at greater cost. If too much fertiliser is used, the yield might even decrease.

The mixed farm has a ready source of organic waste which may only need to be topped up by some artificial fertilisers. The arable farm relies more on artificial fertilisers which are more convenient to use. However, as the costs of production rise, cheaper organic waste becomes more attractive.

Selective breeding produces new varieties, some of which can be grown on marginal land if modern artificial fertilisers are used. The idea of growing new varieties, with the accompanying use of artifical fertilisers, was exported to developing countries such as Brazil and South East Asia to found the 'Green Revolution'. However, with increases in the price of fertiliser production, only the richer landowners could afford to maintain the use of sufficient quantities of artificial fertilisers to maintain a high yield. The poor learnt the hard way that without the extra fertiliser, the new varieties give lower yields than traditional wheats.

■ Organic farming

Nowadays, more farmers and smallholders are beginning to realise the importance of some of the old methods, firmly based on good biology! They find that by using a rotation of different crops with different nutrient demands on the same field in successive years, the cycle of disease can be broken. This avoids the need for chemical pesticides and artificial fertilisers. A crop rotation is typically of three to six years. The pests of one crop are unlikely to survive in the soil until the next time that the crop comes around. A typical four-year rotation is: root crop $\longrightarrow$ cereal $\longrightarrow$ clover $\longrightarrow$ cereal.

The actual crops involved depends on the region of the country. In a cereal-production area the rotation might be: roots $\longrightarrow$ barley $\longrightarrow$ barley $\longrightarrow$ beans $\longrightarrow$ wheat $\longrightarrow$ oats.

In rich silt or fenland the rotation might be: potatoes $\longrightarrow$ sugar $\longrightarrow$ beet $\longrightarrow$ wheat $\longrightarrow$ clover.

To provide natural nitrogen fertiliser a clover crop is included (or the land is left fallow or a grass ley is sown for grazing by farm animals which provide manure) and plant remains are ploughed in to add humus. In this case the rotation might be: potatoes $\longrightarrow$ wheat $\longrightarrow$ clover $\longrightarrow$ sugar $\longrightarrow$ beet $\longrightarrow$ two year ley.

Organic farmers rely on manure and compost to fertilise the land after the removal of a crop. They also use other sources of organic fertiliser (e.g. waste, blood, fish and bone meal). Manure from livestock and compost from plant remains are broken down to humus by decomposers; woodlice, millipedes, earthworms, slugs and snails. Further decay to produce inorganic nutrients is carried out by bacteria and fungi (Fig.1.4, Fig.2.15). These materials provide a slow release of nutrients as they decay. They also separate the soil particles, giving it a better texture by making it more porous and improving aeration, water-holding capacity and drainage. It is then less likely to become compacted by heavy machinery.

 Use library resources to find out more about the Green Revolution.

■ The problems of pests and diseases in a wheat crop

Animal pests (Fig.5.9) have a good time with the bountiful food, hopping from plant to plant instead of having to search over a large area. Some of the pests include slugs and wireworms (larvae of click beetles, *Agriotes obscurus*) which attack the grain after it has been sown. Leatherjackets (the larvae of crane flies, *Tipula* sp.) and wheat stem bulb flies, feed on the crop while it is growing. Eelworms

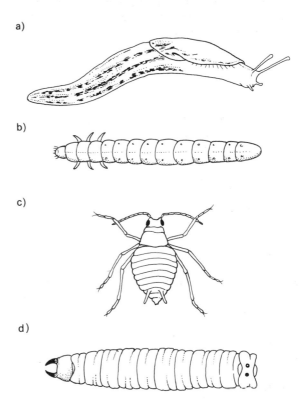

Figure 5.9 Some wheat pests: a) slug, b) wireworm, c) leatherjacket. See also the stem eelworm in Fig 8.3

(nematodes) penetrate the tissues of the roots and stems to feed. Aphids (*Sitobion avenae*) on the leaves and stems insert their stylets into the phloem to suck sap and may transmit viruses at the same time. Larger pests are wood pigeons and rabbits. Ergot fungus (*Claviceps purpurea*) (rust) on damp ears of grain reduces the yield and makes it poisonous (Fig.5.10). Because so many fungi attack wheat, farmers sow grain that has been dressed with fungicide, which may be toxic to seed-eating birds.

Figure 5.10 Ergot (*Claviceps purpurea*) on a wheat ear and (inset) on a single grain

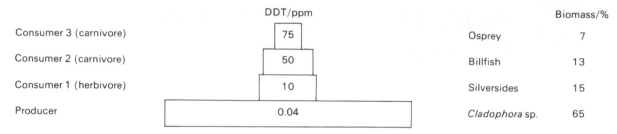

Figure 5.11 The concentration in parts per million (ppm) of DDT and the relative biomass of four trophic levels in a food chain. (Data derived from USA material)

Weeds, such as chickweed, shepherd's purse, dandelion, creeping thistle, poppy, and fat-hen, compete with the crop for light, food and water, reducing crop yield. The weeds in a field are growing in the habitat which suits them best so they flourish. In contrast, crops may not be growing in their natural habitat, they may have been genetically altered and need to be cared for to survive. Too often, recourse is taken to chemicals.

Herbicides are classified according to their mode of action.

• *Contact herbicides* cause rapid scorching of the leaves, killing the shoot (e.g. paraquat and sulphuric acid). If the ground is sprayed with a non-persistent herbicide like paraquat, all the plants are killed. It is absorbed by the leaves, producing toxic peroxides in the cells. It is very toxic to humans and other mammals, causing irreversible lung and kidney damage. Spray drift kills hedges and trees and may affect neighbouring property.

After the herbicide spray has been deactivated in the soil, the wheat grains can be drilled into the unploughed soil where they germinate with no competition. Less energy is required to produce and use herbicides in this way than to plough and cultivate the soil into a seed bed before drilling. This type of cultivation is known as *direct drilling*.

• *Systemic herbicides* are taken up into the tissues. 2-4 dichlorophenoxyacetic acid (commonly known as 2-4D) is a selective herbicide sprayed during early growth. It is absorbed through the leaves of broad-leaved weeds, but not the narrow monocotyledonous leaves of wheat. It acts like an auxin, speeding up the metabolic rate so much that it causes death. This type of herbicide is used on lawns, killing the weeds but not the grass.

• *Residual herbicides* (e.g. simazine) are sprayed on clean soil and they inhibit photosynthesis in the germinating weeds. Simazine works at low concentrations, it is persistent and is believed to have a low toxicity to animals.

■ The controversial use of pesticides

The ideal pesticide:
• is toxic to the pest and harmless to other species.
• persists on the crop to give it long-term protection.
• does not spread into water or into food chains.
• is deactivated by normal metabolic processes in species that are not pests.

No one pesticide has all these properties. Most insecticides are not specific and they kill a whole range of insects, including pollinators and carnivorous species that may eat the pest. Continual repeated use of insecticide stops the predator species ever reaching sufficient numbers to control the pest. In addition, birds and mammals feeding on the poisoned pests concentrate the insecticides in their bodies (Fig.5.11). This has been strikingly demonstrated with the persistent insecticide DDT, a chemical now banned in many developed countries (but still made under licence in developing countries!).

If no pesticides are used, over a number of years balanced populations of insects appear, although these naturally fluctuate with environmental conditions. Organic farmers, using no artificial insecticides, may have a slightly lower yield overall but consumers are often willing to pay higher prices for food that they believe is tastier and free from pesticide contamination.

Q 1. Summarise the case for and against the use of pesticides in terms of a) wildlife populations b) crop yield and c) human health.

2. What are the biological effects of rabbits grazing on downland vegetation?

3. Frequent mowing of a lawn provides an even turf with daisies.
Playing fields are often sprayed with broad-leaf herbicides.

Explain these two statements.

6 PLANTS AS PRODUCERS FOR PROFIT AND PLEASURE

A popular radio programme allows well-known people to fantasise about eight records they would take to a desert island. Imagine we changed the rules and you have been taking part in 'Desert Island Discs' and a kind producer has left you with all the equipment you need to take cuttings and do grafting. You also have, of course, plants typically found growing on a desert island in the tropical Pacific, including coconut palms. As a luxury item you are allowed to select three families of plants and to choose a supply of seeds from just three species in each family. What choices would you make? What cultivation programmes and breeding experiments would you carry out to provide a steady supply of varied and nutritious food? By the time you have finished studying this Chapter, and with the information from Chapters 4 and 5, you should be able to reach a decision.

The word *crop* is used to describe the harvesting of a plant or part of a plant for use by humans for various foods (fruits and vegetables) and materials (wood and paper) as well as to give to domesticated animals as fodder. Two types of plant tissue are mainly of value in a crop plant, the thin-walled parenchyma and the fibrous sclerenchyma and xylem (Chapter 1).

▪ PARENCHYMA CELLS

Parenchyma is used by the plant for storing foods in organs such as tubers, bulbs, seeds and fruits. Stored proteins (polypeptides) and starch (polysaccharides) are in the form of long chain molecules which coil into rounded grains. The parenchyma cell, more or less spherical, with its living contents lining the cell membrane, is a shape that has the maximum volume for its surface area; an ideal storage container. Stored foods are mostly insoluble, and so do not interfere with osmotic processes in the cell. Look under a microscope at cells scraped from the cut surface of a potato in a drop of iodine solution. The starch grains are stored in *plastids* (membrane-bound storage sacs in the cytoplasm) as shown in Fig.6.1.

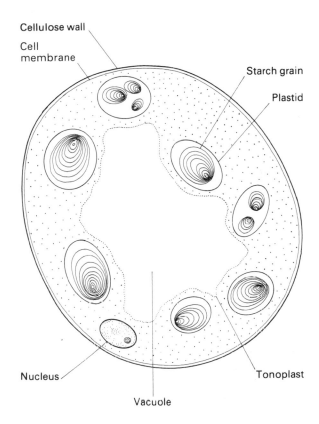

Figure 6.1 Starch grains in a cell of a potato tuber

Many seeds store food in parenchyma, and vegetative structures also make use of parenchyma cells to store food through the winter. These include bulbs, stem tubers, root tubers and fruits.

▪ Bulbs

A bulb is a much reduced stem bearing tightly packed fleshy and scaly leaf bases from the present and the previous year's growth respectively. It is the fleshy leaves that contain the food store. Figure 6.2 illustrates the annual cycle of a daffodil bulb (the cycle of an onion is similar).

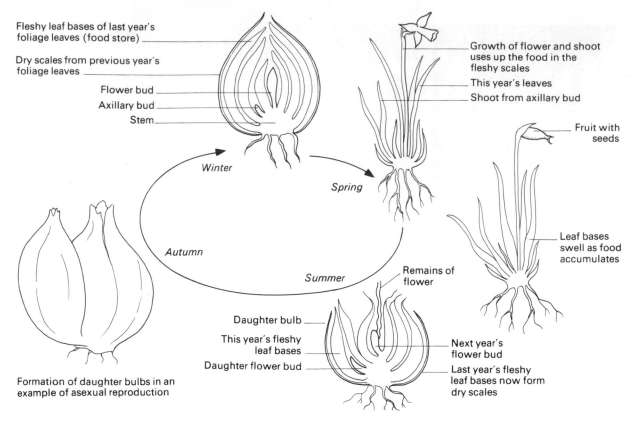

Fleshy leaf bases of last year's foliage leaves (food store)

Dry scales from previous year's foliage leaves

Flower bud

Axillary bud

Stem

Winter

Spring

Autumn

Summer

Growth of flower and shoot uses up the food in the fleshy scales

This year's leaves

Shoot from axillary bud

Fruit with seeds

Leaf bases swell as food accumulates

Remains of flower

Daughter bulb

This year's fleshy leaf bases

Daughter flower bud

Next year's flower bud

Last year's fleshy leaf bases now form dry scales

Formation of daughter bulbs in an example of asexual reproduction

Figure 6.2 Annual cycle of a daffodil bulb (the cycle of the onion bulb is similar)

Q By reference to Fig.6.2, write an account of the stages in the annual cycle of the daffodil bulb. Describe the movement and storage of food in the plant. How does the bulb function as an asexually reproducing structure?

▌ Stem tubers

A stem tuber is a swollen underground stem containing the food store. An example is the potato (Fig.6.3). At the 'eyes', shoots are produced which grow into branches. These are covered with soil when the plant is 'earthed up'. The tips of these underground branches swell with food as it is translocated into them from the leaves, to form a crop of new potatoes. If exposed to the light the tuber develops chlorophyll. (Why?)

Q Draw a diagram to show what happens when the potato plant is 'earthed up'.

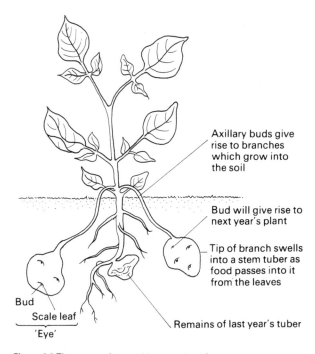

Axillary buds give rise to branches which grow into the soil

Bud will give rise to next year's plant

Tip of branch swells into a stem tuber as food passes into it from the leaves

Bud

Scale leaf

'Eye'

Remains of last year's tuber

Figure 6.3 The potato plant and its annual cycle

Iris rhizomes

Other underground stems (*rhizomes*), which continue the growth of the plant year after year, such as iris rhizomes, may also swell with stored food. The rhizomes of most grasses never become large storage organs as the aerial shoot does not die during winter. Couch is a troublesome garden weed with fast growing and long-lived rhizomes (Fig.6.4).

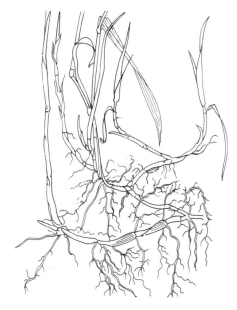

Figure 6.4 Couch rhizomes

Q 1. What evidence have you read to indicate that the potato tuber is a stem and not a root?

2. Why does 'earthing up' increase potato yield?

3. Why does the iris rhizome contain a large store of food whereas that of couch does not?

■ Root tuber

Plants with one main root bearing branches (e.g. the tap root of carrot) or plants with many similar-sized roots (e.g. the adventitious roots of celandine) may become swollen with food by the end of the growing season. The shoot then dies down. The following spring, some of the stored food is used to produce a new shoot. In the case of the biennial carrot, this second year's shoot then flowers and produces seeds and the whole plant dies (Fig.6.5). Celandine, which is a perennial, develops new flowering shoots each year (Fig.1.14).

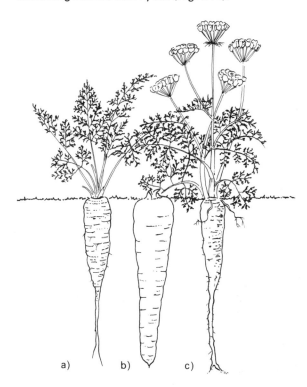

Figure 6.5 The tap root and shoot development of the carrot: a) first year's growth, b) tap root full of food, the shoot having died down at the end of the first year, c) shoot and flowers produced in the second year

Q What happens to the stored food in Fig.6.5b?

■ Fruits

We eat whole fruits or just the seeds within a fruit. The word 'fruit' is probably the most misused botanical term in the English language (Chapter 1). Many 'vegetables' are actually fruits, marrows and runner beans, for example. On the other hand, rhubarb is a leaf stem. Succulent fruits, such as tomatoes and kiwi fruit, are important sources of vitamin C and minerals; peas and beans of protein and fibre. Nuts also contain valuable protein and are therefore a useful addition to a vegetarian diet (Fig.6.6). They also contain unsaturated oils. Apart from the examples mentioned in Chapter 2, other sources of oil are the seeds of maize, sunflower, olives, palm, coconut and oilseed rape (Fig.6.7). For use in margarine some of the oil has to be *hardened* by making it less unsaturated in order to make it less fluid and more spreadable. In addition, plant oils can be used as lubricants and as a fuel.

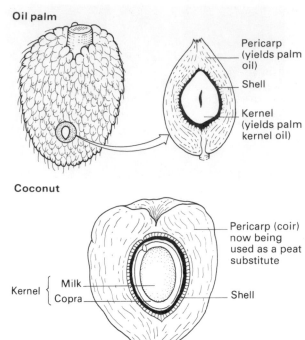

Figure 6.7 Important sources of vegetable oils

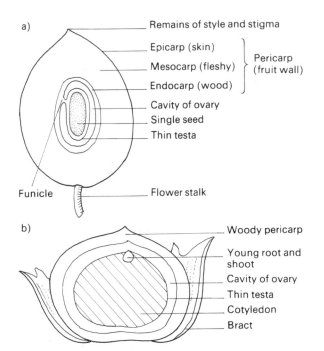

Figure 6.6 a) Vertical section of: a) a drupe; plum (*Prunus* sp.), b) an achene or nut; hazel (*Corylus* sp.). See also the false fruits of apple and strawberry in Fig 1.16 as examples of other important crops

The economic importance of plant storage is demonstrated by the range of plant families whichsupply us with food (Table 6.1). In Great Britain plant consumption (not including cereal and flour products) in 1990 was an average of 2.28 kg of vegetables (1.84 kg fresh and 0.44 kg frozen or preserved) and 0.56 kg of fruit per person per week.

Q For the plants listed in Table 6.1 state which part forms the storage structures, i.e. whether the part we eat is the root, stem, leaf or seed.

Family	Crops
Gramineae	Wheat, oats, barley, rye, rice, maize, sugar cane, bamboo, miller
Leguminoseae	Pease, beans, soya, peanut, alfalfa
Rosaceae	Apple, pear, plum, cherry, apricot, peach, almond, loquat
Crucifereae	Cabbage, sprout, cauliflower, kale, turnip, cress, rape, radish
Palmae	Oil palm, date, coconut, sago, sugar palm

Table 6.1 Plant families and food crops

■ SCLERENCHYMA AND XYLEM

Both sclerenchyma and xylem have thickened cell walls with many layers of long-chain cellulose molecules impregnated with lignin. It is these fibres, teased out into parallel strands, that are used in threads for the manufacture of cloth, rope and furnishings, as well as paper. Wood is used directly in building and furniture or mashed up and reconstituted into chipboard and paper.

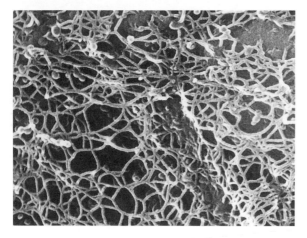

Cellulose microfibrils

■ Wood
It is the xylem and sclerenchyma, constituting the wood of secondarily thickened trees, that provide us with timber. Hard woods (e.g. mahogany, oak, elm and beech) provide a fine grain that takes a deep polish and these timbers are prized for furniture. The source of mahogany is tropical rainforests and increasingly people feel that the wholesale destruction of forest to take out a few mature mahogany trees cannot be justified. Softer, quicker growing timber from conifers, such as the pines, is cheaper and is used where appearance is less important, for roof timbers, pit props and more utilitarian furniture.

The grain in timber is due to the medullary rays running as vertical plates of parenchyma cells along the radii of the trunk, enabling food and water to be carried across the xylem. In a mature tree the central area is the heartwood, made up of fully lignified xylem, non-functional but giving structural strength. Outside this is the sapwood which is functional in water transport. Variation in timber texture is caused by the size of the vessels in spring and autumn. Wood colour is due to the chemicals present, lignin and tannins. The phloem is a thin layer between the sapwood and the bark. When the bark is peeled off, the phloem comes away as well. Deer are not popular in commercial woodland because they strip the bark off young trees, preventing phloem transport, so resulting in the death of the tree.

■ Fibre
Many plants provide fibre for a range of materials. The important ones are described here.

Flax is an annual herb. The fibres are extracted following the microbial breakdown of the soft tissue of stems in a process called *retting*. They are then spun into threads for making linen. Linseed oil comes from the seeds of other species of flax.

Cotton is made from the 'hairs' attached to the seed inside the seed capsule and it is the world's most important textile fibre.

Coir matting is made from the fibres in the husks of coconuts. Now, coir is being marketed as a peat substitute in horticulture.

Jute is a member of the lime family and is grown in Bangladesh and India for its fibre, used in sacking, carpets and linoleum. One species of hemp, is used as a source of fibre for canvas, rope and twine. Another species, sunn hemp, which is a legume, is used for making rope and sacking.

■ PLANTS FOR PLEASURE

The horticultural industry is a big one. You have only to see the growth in the number of garden centres over the last decade to realise that. Why this trend? It is certain that attractive plants in our working and living environment have beneficial psychological effects. All too often, our concrete jungles lack the essential 'green-ness' that unconsciously represents life itself. A soothing environment is said to reduce blood pressure and stress and induce a more relaxed state. Scented flowers are especially important to blind people. Although few house plants are grown for their scent (exceptions being hyacinth and freesia), many scented plants, such as night-scented stock and tobacco, can be grown out-of-doors.

The increase in enthusiasm for gardening, from window boxes to greenhouses, to gardens and allotments, is partially linked to the desire for fresher, more wholesome and organically grown food (Chapter 5) but also the appreciation of the enhancement of flavour contributed by herbs and spices. Many familiar herbs in the cottage garden, such as parsley, rosemary and mint, have been used as ingredients in cooking since the beginning of civilisation.

Gardens differ widely: some people prefer the often small, delicate wild flowers and try to replicate a miniature bit of the British countryside around their homes. Others prefer the more exotic imported species or *cultivars* (varieties maintained by cultivation) in a formal arrangement where weeds have no place. Others have a nostalgia for the old-fashioned cottage garden, a riot of colour in an informal setting, where weeds may be either tolerated or squeezed out by the planted species.

The term *weed*, therefore, has different connotations depending on the type of habitat in which it is found. The definition of a weed as a plant out of place, needs to be qualified by relating it to the habitat concerned. Wild poppies, corncockles and scentless mayweed are weeds in the farmer's wheat field, but wild flowers to the wildlife gardener.

Giant hogweed, a poisonous plant

Conversely, alien garden plants can become noxious weeds, thriving in the countryside. An example is the *giant hogweed*, 3.5 m high and poisonous, which finds waste ground and stream banks to its taste. It is a biennial or triennial plant, introduced to the gardens of Great Britain, by Victorian collectors at the end of the last century, from the Caucasus Mountains in Russia. Its toxic sap, exuded through stiff hairs on the stem and leaves, contains the chemical *fucocoumerin* which

permanently damages the skin's ability to filter out ultraviolet light. The result is permanent sunburn with rashes and blistering occurring every time the skin is exposed to sunlight.

Rhodedondron ponticum, a problem plant

The notorious *Rhododendron ponticum*, with its high germination rate and poisonous nectar, has become a major pest. Grown in gardens, it has now escaped to cover large areas of the hillsides on Exmoor, in Wales and in the west Scotland, killing all other ground cover plants.

The types of plants favoured as decoration can be divided into the curious or strange and the colourful and flamboyant. There is a 'science fiction' unreality in watching some of the fourteen genera of insectivorous plants at work. The venus fly-trap has three hairs on the upper leaf surface. When one is touched, nothing happens, but when the same hair is touched again or two separate hairs are touched within 20 seconds, a response is triggered and the leaf hinge closes - in just one fifth of a second, trapping the prey.

Venus fly trap

In the tropical pitcher plant, the leaf is modified into a pitcher, with the leaf stalk taking over the photosynthetic role. Quite often the hooded top of the pitcher bears coloured lines and patterns,

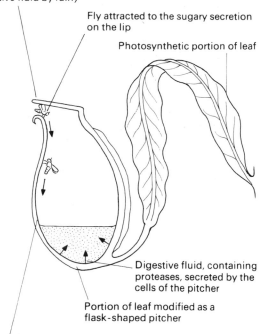

'Lid' (prevents dilution of the digestive fluid by rain)

Fly attracted to the sugary secretion on the lip

Photosynthetic portion of leaf

Digestive fluid, containing proteases, secreted by the cells of the pitcher

Portion of leaf modified as a flask-shaped pitcher

Inside surface covered with tile-like wax scales. These rub off on to the fly's feet which then have no grip and so the fly slides down into the digestive fluid

Figure 6.8 Vertical section of a pitcher plant (*Nepenthes* sp.) to show how insects are caught

lines and patterns, reminiscent of honey guides in flowers. The pitcher plant has a slippery, sugar-coated lip which attracts insects to feed. They lose their footing, the downward-pointing hairs on the inside wall of the pitcher stop them climbing out and they fall into the pool of digestive juices (containing proteases and lipases) at the bottom (Fig.6.8). The enzymes can even break down insect chitin.

British insectivorous plants include the sundew and butterwort both of which have sticky hairs on their leaves. Another insectivorous plant, bladderwort, is a freshwater plant - where the bladders act like lobster pots with one-way openings. Sundews, butterworts and bladderworts all grow in habitats where mineral nutrients, especially nitrogen, are deficient (Fig.6.9).

For most people colour and form are the most important factors in their choice of indoor plants. The colour may be in either the flowers themselves, for example, the many species of begonia and busy Lizzie or in the foliage which can be coloured as in the prayer plant or variegated ivy.

Plants grown for their form may range from climbers to small trees, with dissected or variously shaped leaves to give visually interesting groups when massed. Enterprising businesses, developed over recent years, concentrate on the use of plants for the decoration of public buildings, office foyers, directors' boardrooms and hospital

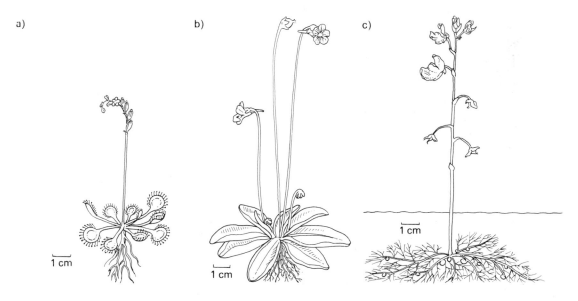

a)   b)   c)

Figure 6.9 British insectivorous plant species: a) round-leaved sundew (*Drosera rotundifolia*), b) common butterwort (*Pinguicula vulgaris*), c) greater bladderwort (*Utricularia vulgaris*)

waiting rooms. Local councils increasingly use bedding plants to add colour to city streets and shopping precincts.

Often, the cultivars we plant have been developed from imported species. These may be difficult to grow and often have to be nurtured to survive the competition with native plants. But how did the gardener's interest in foreign species first arise? The curiosity and acquisitiveness of human beings, as well as an appreciation of the attractiveness of plants and a desire to produce more unusual food crops, sent the early plant collectors abroad. Many of the exotic plants brought back to Britain to the Royal Botanic Gardens, Kew by the early collectors are now within the reach of the amateur gardener. Sir Walter Raleigh (1552-1618) brought the humble potato from North Carolina. After him the Tradescants, royal gardeners, introduced not only Tradescantia but also many others, including Persian lilac, Virginia Creeper, lupins and Michaelmas daisies. Joseph Banks (1743-1820) returned with plants from China, Australia and New Zealand. Other famous collectors include David Douglas (1779-1834) and Charles Darwin (1809-1882). Many plants were discovered and named after these explorers, for example, *Cordyline banksii*, *Berberis darwinii* and Douglas fir. New species can still be discovered in the remote wildernesses of the world and especially in the tropical rainforests where, it is suspected, hundreds of plants have potential as vegetable crops.

The early collectors had little effect on wild environments. They carried away single specimen plants. Nowadays, too many wild plants are plundered from their habitats all over the world for sale to amateur gardeners, and are being brought to the point of extinction, for example, bromeliads from the Amazon forests, cyclamen from Turkey and orchids from all over the world. Many countries now impose import restrictions on the rarer groups of plants; for example, although Britons are allowed to bring in 2 kg of plant material, this material cannot include orchids.

This demand requires a cheap supply of enormous numbers of all types of plants and methods of artificial propagation and selective breeding have been developed to satisfy the market, without denuding the environment.

David Douglas (1779-1834)

Douglas fir

Sexual	Asexual
Involves fusion of gametes	No fusion of gametes
Two parents involved (may be in same flower)	One parent plant only
Offspring show variation	Offspring identical with parent
Results in seed production	No seeds produced
Offspring dispersed from parents	Offspring usually attached to parent or later detached

Table 6.2 Differences between sexual and asexual reproduction

Q Asexual propagation, both natural and artificial, can be used to produce large numbers of offspring with a constant phenotype (the appearance of the plant due to its genetic make-up). Explain how this is achieved and why it is important to the horticultural market.

■ ARTIFICIAL PROPAGATION

The branching rhizome of iris produces shoots along its length, i.e. vegetative propagation. Cutting the rhizome into pieces to plant separately is an example of artificial propagation. The main methods of artificial propagation include leaf cuttings, stem cuttings, root cuttings and grafts.

■ Leaf cuttings
A leaf cut off an African violet will root when planted. Leaves of begonia can be rooted in the same way or even cut into pieces to plant, as long as each piece has some of the midrib.

Leaf cutting of a begonia

■ Stem cuttings
The cut shoot of a stem should, when planted, produce roots at the lower end and continue shoot growth at the upper. This can happen because there are undifferentiated, meristematic cells present throughout the life of a plant which can develop into specialised cells. Cuttings can be either from this year's growth, known as soft cuttings (e.g. chrysanthemum), or from last year's growth, known as hard cuttings (e.g. blackcurrant). Jasmine cuttings produce new roots very easily, other species take a long time to become established. The investigation below shows you how to take a cutting.

INVESTIGATION

Take soft cuttings from a willow. Treat half the cuttings with rooting powder before planting. Plant the rest directly. Compare the time taken for roots to establish in each sample.

Willow trees root readily. Some people who use willow for fence posts are surprised to find them growing into trees!

a)
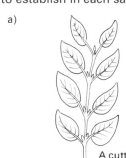
A cutting is removed from the plant and put immediately into a polythene bag until used

b)

The stem is cut off below a node and the lower leaves are removed. The stem is dipped in hormone rooting powder

c) The cutting is planted in damp compost and enclosed in a polythene bag to keep it moist

■ Root cuttings

This is not a common practice but we can all see evidence of it in our gardens. Just try chopping up the tap root of a dandelion as you dig and wait to see how many small dandelion plants result.

■ Grafts

A graft is the fusion of vegetative parts of two plants so that they grow as one, in order to combine the best characteristics of the two (Fig.6.10). The lower part is the *rootstock* or *stock*, the upper part the *scion*.

For example, many apple varieties are grown on dwarfing rootstocks so that the final tree will not be too big and small gardens can have the luxury of several fruit trees. A dwarf apple rootstock, called M27, was developed at East Malling Research Station (UK). It produces, for example, Bramley trees that can be planted commercially about one metre apart, reaching a width of about 90 cm when ten years old, so increasing yields and ease of harvesting.

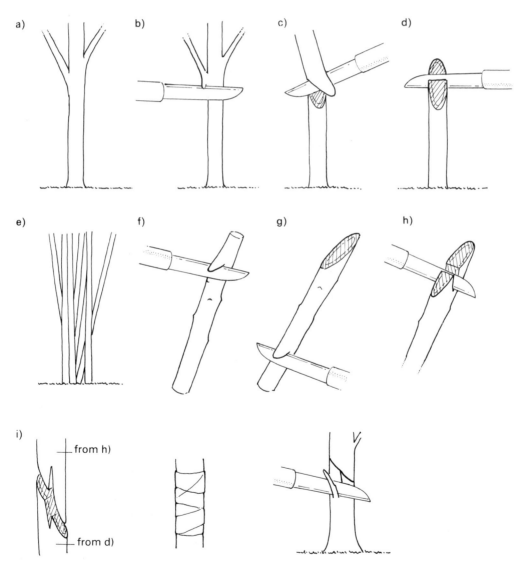

Figure 6.10 Making a whip and tongue graft: steps a) to d) show the preparation of the stock, steps e) to i) show the preparation of the scion. Give a brief description of the stages from a) through to i)

It is possible to create a 'family' tree by grafting a number of different varieties, e.g. both cooking and eating apples, on to the same tree.

Grafting involves skill and care and is therefore more often used commercially than by the ordinary gardener. It involves fusion of stock and scion so that the scion receives water and food materials enabling it to grow. It is a procedure restricted mainly to dicotyledons. (Why?) While the graft is 'taking', the cut surfaces must be bound closely together to prevent water loss and invasion by disease organisms. At first, *callus* (undifferentiated) tissue forms at the point of contact between stock and scion by mitosis of both cambial tissues. The joint is cemented together by substances such as *pectins* and other cell-forming polysaccharides secreted by undamaged neighbouring cells. Ends of vessels in the vascular tissue break down and rebuild transport channels through the join. New cells differentiate into cambium where they line up with the cambium of scion and stock, forming new xylem and phloem to complete the connection.

Grafting is a valuable technique because both the scion and the stock retain their own characteristics. Many roses, for example, are heavily-flowering or scented scions growing on a strong, disease-resistant rootstock.

■ Selective breeding

A great increase in knowledge has been made in recent years in the production of new disease-resistant and high-yielding varieties of crop plants to feed the increasing human population and to provide new varieties to please the eye. In the last 50 years, two important tools in the armoury of the plant breeder have been *tissue culture* (*micropropagation*) and *genetic engineering*. These new methods achieve the same results as selective breeding but more precisely, quickly, and independently of the seasons, as genes can be selected and put in place artificially instead of waiting for a chance combination to arise in cross-fertilisation (Fig.6.11).

■ Tissue culture

Once a horticulturist has produced an attractive F_1 hybrid, usually after several years of selective breeding, he or she wants many identical plants quickly for commercial sale. Tissue culture achieves this by artificial asexual reproduction in which large numbers of offspring are produced and

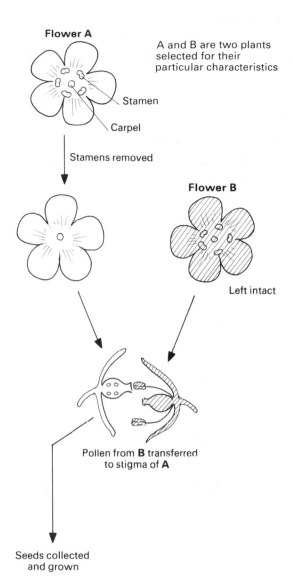

Figure 6.11 Cross-pollination in plant breeding

variation is eliminated. These offspring with a constant *genotype* (genetic make-up) are known as *clones*.

The general procedure is: remove meristematic tissue from the parent plant; grow these groups of cells on a suitable nutrient agar in sterile bottles. (Growers tend to be secretive about their special recipes for these nutrient media.) In the right conditions, the cells grow into a mass of undifferentiated cells and further development produces a number of tiny plantlets which can be separated and grown on in conventional compost in pots.

A young genetically-engineered tobacco plant, *Nicotina tabacum*, grows on special culture medium

It is essential that the right balance of auxin and cytokinin is used in the culture bottles. The interaction between cytokinin and other plant growth substances was demonstrated in the 1950s by Skoog. Stoog's experiments showed that:
• a callus of tobacco exposed to 0.2 mg dm^{-3} of cytokinin continues callus growth,
• an exposure to a lower cytokinin level of 0.02 mg dm^{-3} starts the growth of roots,
• a higher level of 0.5 mg dm^{-3} initiates shoot growth.

Skoog concluded that a high auxin to cytokinin ratio promoted root growth and a high cytokinin to auxin ratio promoted the growth of shoots from lateral buds. Many plants, including begonia and coleus, are now produced for the horticultural market in this way. Ninety per cent of gerbera plants are produced by micropropagation, and food plants produced in the same way include banana, date and oil palm.

■ Genetic engineering

Genes can be transferred from one plant to another by use of the soil bacterium, *Agrobacterium radiobacter* var. *tumefaciens* which gains entry in a wide range of dicotyledons through a wound (Fig.6.12). It stimulates tumour (*gall*) growth and once established, the tumour cells, transformed by the bacterial DNA, continue to divide. The genetic change in the host cells occurs as a result of the insertion of a bacterial plasmid which can be genetically engineered to carry the desired genes.

Such genes, appearing in the resulting tumour cells (*gall*) are passed on to the progeny by tissue culture, the resulting new plants being known as *transgenic plants*. In this process, the bacterium acts as a *vector*, carrying the new gene into the host.

It is hoped that useful genes, such as those controlling disease resistance, colour and flavour, can be inserted at will. To this end, experiments with *A. tumefaciens* have been carried out with tomato, potato, tobacco, petunia and sunflower. It is possible that this technique can be used with other dicotyledonous crops, including soya beans and oilseed rape.

In addition there has been some limited success with recombinant viruses and, more excitingly, with vectorless transfer of DNA which does not rely on infection to introduce new genes. This system entails removing the cellulose wall, then making the protoplast membrane of the host cell 'leaky' by a pulse of high-voltage electricity (*electroporation*) whilst being incubated with foreign DNA. (Apart from electroporation, treatment of protoplasts with polyethylene glycol also makes them more receptive to DNA uptake.) Initially, around 10% transformation was achieved in tobacco, sunflower and petunia and from the engineered cells, transgenic plants have been grown by tissue culture. Electroporation and treatment with polyethylene glycol is now being used in other food crops, including rice and maize.

This method has also been applied successfully to potatoes but much work still remains to be done, especially in relation to disease resistance. It is now possible to produce hybrids by fusing leaf cell **protoplasts**, a process known as *somatic hybridisation*. The technique has been useful in combining the gene giving resistance to the virus causing leaf curl in the wild potato, with cultivated high-

---

protoplasts   a plant cell from which the cellulose cell wall has been removed (by using a cellulase enzyme). In the right growth medium and under the right conditions, leaf protoplasts can be cultured so that they give rise to a callus of undifferentiated cells and, eventually, a plant with an identical genetic make-up to the parent cell. In this way hundreds of plants can be cloned from a single leaf! After suitable treatment, two protoplasts from different varieties can be made to fuse and form a new hybrid plant, hence *somatic hybridisation* yielding potatoes. There is the possibility also of producing varieties resistant to specific insect pests or to fit into particular environmental conditions. A new method being tried is the bombardment of meristematic or embryonic tissues with DNA-coated particles using either a shotgun explosion or electric discharge as the motive power. This technique has been successfully used in the soya bean. These processes have enormous potential for producing disease-resistant and high-yielding plants - useful for feeding the world's growing population in developing countries.

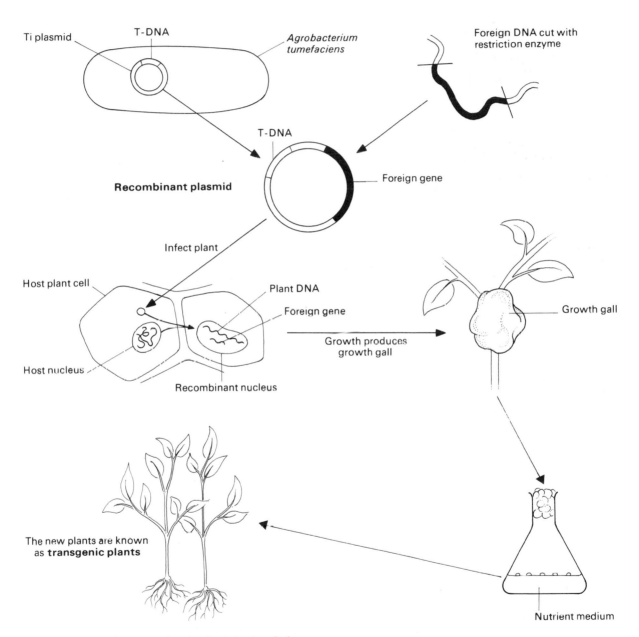

Figure 6.12 Transferring genes using *Agrobacterium tumefaciens*

USE AND MISUSE OF PLANTS

Tropical rain forest, lush vegetation

Amazonian rain forest, destruction of trees to create transport links for oil industry

The potential of the plant kingdom to supply foods and chemicals for the benefit of humans is enormous. Unfortunately, this resource is often misused. Not only may the chemicals that plants produce be abused but the plants and their habitats may be destroyed. Why the destruction? You will already know that seldom is it the local populations that destroy, but rather others who come in to exploit the area for commercial profit, before departing, often leaving a damaged ecosystem behind. A small native tribe such as the Xavante living in a vast Amazonian forest, or remote islanders in the Pacific know that their survival depends on the long-term conservation of plants, their harvest is non-destructive in the long term.

Some plants become particularly important to the local people because they have many uses. The baobab tree is one such multipurpose plant; we can get rope from its bark, food and medicines from the leaves, drink from the fruit pulp, oil from its seeds. Its trunk is a container for water or storing dry materials and the dead trunk is even used to contain and mummify dead bodies!

Baobab (*Adansonia digitata*)

The coconut tree trunk produces wood for canoes, building and carving into bowls, and leaves for thatching and for weaving into mats. (Fibre from young leaves is used for finely-woven hats and baskets.) The fruit has many uses. Fibre from the outer coat (*coir*) is used for matting, the shell as a container, while the nut is used for food, after drinking the 'milk'. Oil is extracted by squeezing the pulp through a network of fibre retrieved from the base of old leaves. It is used for cooking, lighting and as an anti-sunburn cream! Coir is being developed and marketed as a peat substitute. (This use of a waste product could help to preserve the threatened UK peatland habitats.)

Coconut tree

From the dawn of history, people have looked to plants for real or imaginary means of healing. Witch doctors and their magic must have relied, to a large extent, on a knowledge of human psychology as much as on the known efficacy of certain plants to cure, but we are becoming increasingly aware that many tribal medicines do work. Certainly, many remote tribes rely on the native plants for contraceptives and drugs to fight particular diseases. It is observations such as these that are the essential starting points for pharmaceutical companies in their search for new drugs for our benefit. They extract the biologically active ingredient, determine its chemical structure and then synthesise it in the laboratory. After tests and, perhaps, modification of the original structure, a new drug may be marketed. Today few drugs are sold in the Western world that are obtained directly from plants. But, because the number of chemicals is so vast, pharmaceutical companies could not afford a random search for a new drug. They all rely on clues from primitive usage. This is yet another reason for the conservation of the natural forests and their indigenous inhabitants in all parts of the world. For example, seventy percent of the 3000 plants identified by the United States of America National Cancer Institute as having anti-cancer properties come from a rainforest. Alkaloids in the rosy periwinkle (*Catharanthus roseus*) improve the survival chances of a child suffering from leukaemia from 19% to 80%. Other sugar-shaped alkaloids such as castanospermine (from alexa beans) may be useful in combating AIDS. Biochemists have shown that castanospermine reduces the ability of human immunodeficiency virus (HIV) to infect cultured cells. Reserpine used to treat schizophrenia, anxiety and hypertension comes from the snakeroot plant of India's monsoon forests.

In Europe, up to mediaeval times, the only books on plants were called 'herbals', reflecting the use of plants in medicine. Countryfolk, even in this century, were using herbs as remedies, for example feverfew for migraine. The names of some of our common plants reflect this use, for example woundwort, selfheal, liverwort and eyebright.

Remedies from plants: feverfew (*Tanacetum parthenum*)

The history of some of these plant products can be fascinating. Although it was probably well known to natives beforehand, the anti-malarial drug quinine from cinchona bark was discovered about 1638 when it was used to cure a fever of the Countess of Chinchon, wife of the Spanish Viceroy of Peru. Linnaeus later named the tree *Cinchona officinalis* after the Countess but got the spelling wrong! Felling of the wild trees in the Andes continued until the mid-nineteenth century, when seeds were sent to India and Indonesia to establish plantations for the commercial production of the antimalarial drug quinine. *Cinchona ledgeriana* gives the highest yield, up to 16% in the bark, but nowadays artificial derivatives are used.

Cinchona sp. growing at about 2000 m altitude in the Andes of Ecuador

A few examples serve to demonstrate the wide range of uses of drugs from plants. One of the most notorious drug plants is the opium poppy, used as early as 4000 years ago. Its phloem sap (*latext*) contains more than thirty alkaloids, i.e. compounds of carbon, hydrogen, oxygen and nitrogen. Morphine is one of these compounds and heroin is an artificial derivative. These drugs are used medicinally as painkillers; they are similar to *endorphins* (natural painkillers produced in the brain) and were used as sleep inducers, even for babies, until it was realised how addictive they are. Similarly, cocaine, from the leaves of coca, has been replaced as an anaesthetic in dentistry by the related synthetics procaine and novocaine.

Digitalin is a heart stimulant extracted from the foxglove. It is a glycoside, a combination of an active organic molecule and a sugar, and it is used to restore the heartbeat after cardiac arrest.

Belladonna produces atropine which dilates the pupils. This is useful in eye examination and surgery. Its name (*bella* meaning beautiful and *donna* meaning woman) gives a clue to its original use by Spanish women to make their eyes large and sparkling.

Ginseng, from the roots of *Panax quinquefolium*, is greatly valued in China as a cure for almost everything. Perhaps the herbalists were attracted to it because the roots are supposed to look like the human figure!

Ancient Mayan priests and some witches in Britain probably used hallucinogens to send them into trances and produce visions to impress their audiences. Covens may have used hypnotic drugs to induce mass hypnosis in rituals. This probably accounts for stories of witches flying. Such practices must have been horribly dangerous as well as resulting in addiction. Hallucinogens include LSD (lysergic acid) from morning glory and ergot (the reproductive body of the fungus *Claviceps purpurea*, Fig.5.17), and mescaline from the peyote cactus. All these drugs probably interfere with the activity of *noradrenalin* (a transmitter substance) in the brain. Ergot also causes muscle spasm. In earlier times it was used by midwives in a diluted form to accelerate labour. Farmers fear the appearance of this fungal pest in fodder as it causes cattle to abort.

In fighting your enemies or killing animals for food, there was a range of plant poisons that could be used. Probably curare is the best known. It comes from the leaves of *Chondodendron tomentosum* and it interferes with nerve impulse transmissions when it enters the blood, such as through an arrow wound. The active chemical is still used as a muscle relaxant in surgery and in treating tetanus and rabies.

Plants may produce pleasurable effects. Alcohol (ethanol) is obtained from the fermentation of plant juices by yeasts (anaerobic respiration). The process is known worldwide and juices are used from a wide variety of fruits and flowers containing sugar. Alcohol can be a stimulant or a depressant depending on the individual's reaction. Excess alcohol damages the liver (cirrhosis). Birds and insects can get drunk on alcohol present in decaying and rotting fruit.

Caffeine is found in tea, coffee and in smaller quantities in cocoa. The latter also contains another alkaloid, theobromine, which is less stimulating than caffeine. Excess caffeine may produce sleeplessness and may be a contributory cause of migraine. An ingredient of 'Mormon tea', drunk by the American pioneers, is the stimulant ephedrine (from *Ephedra sinica*), used by hay fever sufferers because it contracts the nasal membranes. Nicotine is an alkaloid stimulant found in tobacco leaves. It is addictive and very poisonous when taken internally and it can also be absorbed through the skin.

Essential oils, such as bergamot, sandalwood, lavender and rose are used in the traditional medicines of the Far East as well as in aromatherapy and massage, ancient techniques that are experiencing a resurgence in the Western world. They are also used in the manufacture of perfumes. Dried plant parts and oils form the sweet-scented pot pourri. Many cosmetics include artificial chemicals based on real flower scents.

Plant pigments were used extensively in the dyeing of cloth. Alder bark produces a brown or black dye, depending on the quantity used; birch bark produces brown; cornflowers blue; dogwood bark produces a bright red colour; golden rod yields yellow. The famous woad of the Ancient Briton produces varying shades of blue (Fig.7.1). Another old dye from madder (Fig.7.2) produces red to purple colours.

Women workers harvesting tea on a tea plantation in Kandy, Sri Lanka

A cocoa tree (*Theobroma cacao*) showing unripe cocoa pods growing from the trunk

Workers harvesting a crop of tobacco in Malawi, Africa

1 cm

Figure 7.1 Woad (*Isatis tinctoria*)

Figure 7.2 Wild madder (*Rubia peregrina*)

Plant food additives used as colourings, flavourings, preservatives, and stabilisers, are given codes known as E numbers. In the past, we relied solely on herbs and spices and the natural colour in foods to give them gastronomic appeal. Recently, the manufacture of artificial colours and flavourings was big business, but concern about the effects of these additives is beginning to limit their use. Some natural colours (and their E numbers) include carotene (E160a) from carrots and tomatoes, and annatto (E160b), a yellow to red-coloured dye from the seed coats of a tropical tree (*Bixa orellana*). Curcumin (E100) from turmeric rhizome is the yellow colour used in curries. Compounds E400 - E405 are extracted from seaweeds, particularly the oarweeds. These are alginates which are used in jellies, thickeners and agar for microbiological nutrient media. Many are used to stabilise emulsified foods, e.g. locust or carob bean gum (E410). E412-416 are other natural gums.

Pectin (E440a) is used to help jams to set. It is the polysaccharide that cements plant cells together. Commercial pectin comes from apple pulp which is a residue from cider making.

WHEN THINGS GO WRONG

Because we rely on plants so much, any damage to them by diseases and pests is of vital importance to us.

Pathogens (disease–causing organisms) may be bacteria, viruses or fungi. Many are specific to particular plants, which means that the pathogen must be able to 'recognise' the plant. Pathogens cause *symptoms* that may result in death but often in a *parasitic* association, the host plant survives. An inefficient parasite which does not reproduce effectively or manage to infect other hosts, risks extinction. One that causes too much damage to the host faces the same risk. Survival for both host and parasite depends on a fine balance in their relationship and in the competition for food.

▮ BACTERIAL DISEASES OF PLANTS

These include the so-called soft rots, blights or wilts. An example is *Phytomonas fabae* which spreads through the cortex at the base of a bean plant stem, breaking down the cell walls so that the plant collapses. This soft rot is spread by seeds which contain the bacterium inside the testa, so treating the outside of the seed with a disinfectant does not help. Sometimes death is caused by the blockage of the vascular system by colonies of bacteria and the toxic slime they produce. There are no bean varieties resistant to this bacterium, but crop rotation (page 71) helps to break the cycle of infection.

▮ VIRAL DISEASES OF PLANTS

Viruses are parasites that take over the control of a cell by inserting their own DNA, with widely varying effects. There is no cure for virus diseases in plants, all that can be done with harmful ones is to stop the spread by burning the affected plants. Some viruses (*latent viruses*) cause no apparent problem to the plant. Many of the stripes and blotches on the petals of some tulips are caused by viruses. These viruses were only recently identified because it is now possible to grow virus-free plants. The colourful effects are often desired by horticulturists.

Colour patterns in tulips caused by the tulip breaking virus. 'Breaking' results in the loss of the red pigment (anthocyanin) but the plant is not destroyed

Viruses are named after the damage they cause, hence we have *cucumber mosaic* and *passion fruit woodiness*. Many disease symptoms are similar to those caused by bacteria and fungi, such as cankers, dwarfing and premature leaf fall. In trees, only a part of the plant may be affected and symptoms can disappear with leaf fall.

Tomatoes infected with the tobacco mosaic virus (TMV) show 'fern-leaf' effects; the decreased leaf area and loss of chlorophyll resulting in a

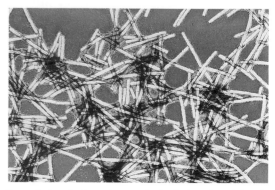

Transmission electron micrograph of rod-shaped particles of tobacco mosaic virus

reduction of photosynthesis and crop yield. This virus is transmitted by insect vectors, commonly aphids. The usual treatment is to burn the affected plants and then restock with certified virus-free plants. Such plants can be grown by tissue culture in a sterile medium. A heat treatment method for plant tissues has been developed at East Malling and Long Ashton Research Stations in the UK. After treatment the growth of new plant material outstrips infection by the virus resulting in virus-free *scions* (plant cuttings for grafting). It has been used most successfully with apples, plums, pears and cherries.

■ FUNGAL DISEASES OF PLANTS

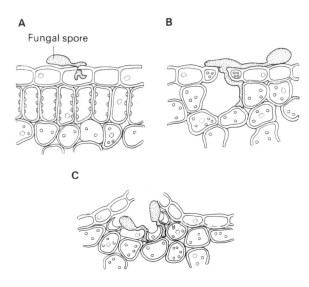

Figure 8.1 Methods of infection by fungal spores: a) through an epidermal cell, b) through a stoma, c) through a wound

Fungi feed *saprobiotically* by secreting enzymes onto their food and absorbing the solute products.

Fungal spores can infect a plant by penetrating the epidermis, or by entering through stomata or wounds (Fig.8.1). Spores of *Phytophthora infestans*, which causes potato blight, send germinating hyphae into the epidermis where they infect the mesophyll cells (Fig.8.2). The first signs of a diseased plant are dark green patches on the leaves which rapidly turn dark brown as the leaf tissue dies. The infection spreads to the tubers which decay and rot. A whole potato field can be

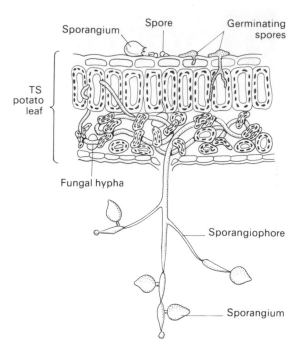

Figure 8.2 Potato blight (Phytophthora infestanus) life cycle. Air-borne sporangia release spores which germinate in the film of water on the leaf surface. Their hyphae penetrate the epidermis, attack the mesophyll cells, and eventually emerge from the stomata bearing new infective sporangia

infected within two weeks. The best control is either to spray the growing plants with **fungicide**, or to remove and burn any diseased plants.

Rusts (*Puccinia* spp. and *Claviceps purpurea*) are the cause of one of the most dangerous cereal fungal diseases. The spores develop in spore sacs (*asci*) in the ears and feeds on the grains heterotrophically, reducing the amount of viable grain (page 68). Smuts (*Ustilago* spp.) also have this effect but they also produce black, powdery spores on the plant which reduces its photosynthetic activity.

---

fungicide a chemical used to kill fungi. There are two types: a) contact fungicide (e.g. Bordeaux mixture) which is sprayed on the surface of seeds or plants and kills any fungal spores it comes in contact with, and b) systematic fungicide (e.g. Benomyl) which is taken up by the plant's transport system and kills any fungal hyphae that are present in the plant tissue

---

Many species of bedding plants and vegetables, e.g. antirrhinum, cress and cabbage, succumb to a fungus infection known as *damping–off*. The cause is a soil-borne fungus (e.g. *Pythium* sp.) which thrives in waterlogged acid soil, with a temperature of about 15°C. The fungus spreads slowly through the soil to infect young plants, invading and digesting the tissues (particularly those at soil level), with the result that the seedling collapses. If it survives, by the autumn the infected plant appears stunted, feeble, and yellow with purplish fungal hyphae over the base of the stem. Damage by the fungus is often followed by bacterial rot. Treatment is by burning the affected plants and avoiding the use of the ground for the same species for 3-4 years. Crop rotation can help here.

The adult elm bark beetle (*Scolytus scolytus*) which carries the fungal spores of Dutch elm disease

Dutch elm disease is caused by a fungus (*Ceratocystis ulmi*) carried by elm bark beetles which lay their eggs in crevices in the bark. The disease was first recorded in Britain in 1927, with only sporadic outbreaks, before the new more virulent strain was imported with Canadian logs in the 1960s. As a result, most of the elm trees in hedges in southern Britain were lost, which changed the appearance of the countryside. There were probably earlier epidemics, which perhaps accounts for the reputation elm has for shedding branches. The fungus produces yeast-like cells which are carried under the bark by the larva of the beetle as it chews fan-shaped tunnels in its search for food. It is here that the fungal spores are produced, and infection spreads rapidly through the xylem vessels

Tunnels made by the elm bark beetle under the bark of a Dutch elm

of the tree. Symptoms of the disease are yellowing and browning of the foliage followed by wilting, defoliation and finally death.

When the larva *metamorphoses* into an adult beetle and leaves the tree, it acts as a vector, infecting other trees with the spores carried on its body. Treatment involves felling the tree, stripping off the bark and burning it. Other methods have been used to protect more valuable trees, for example by several annual injections of systemic fungicide, such as Benomyl.

Resistance to fungal infection can be a general one, in which the plant reacts to a range of fungi, or it can be directed against a particular fungal pathogen. This *specificity* means that new strains of host species can be developed which are resistant to a particular pathogen, e.g. various cereal species resistant to rusts, and some varieties of potato resistant to potato blight.

Resistance in the host may be due to a particular gene which can be bred into a strain and by which pathogen molecules are recognised. At sites of infection, host cells release substances which destroy the pathogen, whereas the non-resistant host does not react. We must assume that the host plant can recognise a type of pathogen molecule.

The presence of *fungi* in food crops is a serious source of food poisoning. Fungi produce poisons called *mycotoxins*, the most dangerous, cancer-inducing one being aflotoxin, which can be found in contaminated peanuts and cereals. Many free-living toadstools are poisonous, e.g. the genus *Amanita* (see the picture of the fly agaric overleaf).

The poisonous fly agaric (*Amanita muscaria*) with its spectacular warning colours (white scaly patches on red) growing on a woodland floor. *A. muscaria* is not normally lethal but will induce hallucinations. Fungi are important decomposers

We make deliberate use of some fungal species, e.g. mushroom (*Psalliota campestris*), yeasts in brewing and baking, and a species of *Penicillium* which is used to produce the streaks of colour in blue-vein cheeses. Sir Alexander Fleming produced his first antibiotic from *Penicillium*.

A *mycorrhiza* is a symbiotic relationship between two organisms, for example, a fungus and a tree. The fungus provides the tree with nutrients from the soil, the fungal hyphae making an intimate contact with the root tissues, acting as root hairs and increasing the surface area for absorption. In return, the hyphae take nutrients from the roots. It has been shown that some trees, e.g. Scots pine will not grow normally in the wild without

Scots pine (*Pinus sylvestris*)

Scots pine tree roots infected with mycorrhizal fungus (*Phaeolus schweintzii*)

mycorrhiza. However, they can be cultivated successfully without the fungus, presumably where there are sufficient nutrients available. Indeed, where the soil is infertile, mycorrhizal fungi have been deliberately introduced to aid tree growth.

One fungus, *Trichoderma viride*, is very antagonistic to the silver leaf fungus, and can be made use of to protect fruit trees. *Trichoderma* needs to be established in the tissues of the tree early on for the protection against silver leaf to be built up. The other advantage of *Trichoderma* is that it itself is quite resistant to fungicides, so a combination treatment (containing the fungus and a fungicide) can be used.

Scientists at Long Ashton Research Station have developed pruning shears with attached reservoirs of fungicide and *Trichoderma* mixture. When a tree is pruned the cut surface will be sealed with the fungicide (for immediate protection) and the fungus (for longer term protection)! Flowering plants are host to a wide range of **epiphytes**, *semi-parasites* and *parasites*.

> **epiphyte** a plant growing on another plant without causing the host plant any harm. The epiphyte uses the host plant for support

Little is known of the interactions between host and epiphyte. Polypody (*Polypodium* sp.), the fern that grows on the branches of beech and other trees, can also be found growing on walls and hedge banks.

Polypody (*Polypodium vulgare*) growing as an epiphyte on an oak tree

Parasites, for example dodder (*Cuscuta* sp.) on heather, form close associations with the host. Root-like *haustoria* grow into the stem of the heather (*Erica* sp.) and tap off food and water from its phloem and xylem. The mature dodder plant has tiny creamy-white scale leaves (it has no chlorophyll and hence no photosynthesis!) but produces large numbers of seeds in the round

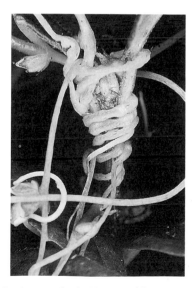

The stem of a plant entwined with dodder (*Cuscuta americana*)

clusters of flowers. Seedlings perish if early contact is not made with a host plant. The developing shoot carries out circular movements in search of the host. Presumably the seedling recognises the stem of a heather plant in some way, then twists around it and pushes haustoria into its tissues.

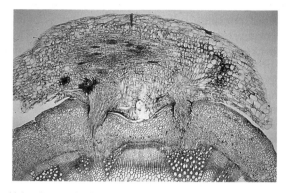

Light micrograph of a lesser dodder, *Cuscuta epithymum*, (top) attached to a host (bottom). Suckers (*haustoria*) penetrate the tissues of the host and 'steal' organic substances as well as water and salts

Plants also act as host to a large number of animal parasites or animals seeking shelter, food or somewhere to lay their eggs. The damage animals do exposes host tissues to infection by other pathogens. The oak tree is host to a large number of insects that induce *gall* formation. Inside a green oak marble gall lives the larva of a wasp, *Andricus kollari,* whose small round exit hole can be seen in an old brown woody gall. The gall is formed as a defence mechanism by the tree. Tissues grow around the wasp egg, cutting it off from the rest of the tree and isolating the problem.

Oak marble gall on an oak twig

CHAPTER 9

FURTHER QUESTIONS

A number of questions have been asked in the text of this book and most of them are of the type that are set as part of an advanced examination. Some questions that have actually appeared in recent examinations now follow.

1 (a) Describe with practical details how you would perform an experiment to show a phototropic response in the shoot of a plant. (8)
(b) Explain how hormones (growth substances) are involved in photoperiodic behaviour in plants. (6)
(*London A-Level, 1988*)

2 (a) Describe the roles of plant growth regulators. (16)
(b) Suggest uses of plant growth regulators in agriculture and horticulture.
(*London AS, 1991*)

3 (a) Define alternation of generations in plants. (4)
(b) Make a table showing the main differences between the Pteridophyta and Spermatophyta (i.e. the Filicinophyta and Angiospermophyta). (7)
(*Wales A-level, 1991*)

4 You are required to make an accurate estimate of the number of stomata in the lower epidermis of a leaf. Describe how you would (a) prepare an epidermal strip (3); (b) set up a microscope to view this strip under high power (5); (c) estimate the total number of stomata present in the lower epidermis of the whole leaf. (7)
(*London A-level, alternative to assessment, 1991*)

5 Genetic improvement of winter wheat.

Table 9.1 shows the results of a recent experiment which compared the five major varieties of winter wheat introduced to British agriculture between the years 1908 and 1980. The different varieties were grown under the same conditions for the purpose of the comparison; total biomass of the plants and the grain yield were measured. From these results the harvest index was calculated to determine the extent of the improvement in winter wheat. The harvest index is the ratio of grain yield to total biomass.
(a) (i) Complete Table 9.1 by calculating the harvest index for the two varieties Maris Huntsman and Norman. (2)

Variety	Year of introduction	Mean plant height cm	Grain yield/ t per ha*	Total biomass/ t per ha*	Harvest index
Little Joss	1908	142	6.0	16.5	0.36
Holdfast	1935	126	6.0	16.5	0.36
Capelle Desprez	1953	110	6.7	15.9	0.42
Maris Huntsman	1972	106	7.5	16.3	–
Norman	1980	84	8.7	17.1	–

Table 9.1 *t per ha = tonnes per hectare
Source: Exploited Plants: Wheat, F.G.H. Lupton, *Biologist* 32 (2) 1985

(ii) Describe the main trends shown in Table 9.1. (3)
(b) (i) Define the term *biomass*. (2)
(ii) In the light of the information given in the table explain why the harvest index is a good indicator of the productivity of wheat. (3)
(iii) Explain how the improvement in harvest index shown in the table has been achieved. (3)
(c) The varieties of winter wheat were all grown under the same conditions. State *two* precautions that would be taken in a carefully controlled comparison of this kind. Explain why the precautions you give are necessary. (4)
(d) The introduction of the combine harvester has led to increased yields of grain. Suggest a reason for this. (2)
(e) List *three* features of wheat, other than those given in Table 9.1, which might be selected by plant breeders. (3)
(f) The wild grass *Aegilops ventricosa* has been used extensively in wheat breeding programmes. Explain why it is important to maintain populations of wild grasses for future improvement of wheat. (3)
(*COSSEC AS, 1990*)

6(a) Distinguish between passive and active uptake of ions by cells. (5)
(b) Describe the uptake of water and ions in root hair cells. (5)
(c) Comment on the importance of turgidity for herbaceous flowering plants. (5)
(*London A-level, 1991*)

7 With reference to angiosperms (flowering plants) write notes under the following headings: (a) support in a young plant stem (3); (b) formation of secondary xylem in a stem during a growing season (8); and (c) photoperiodic effects (6).
(*Scotland Higher, 1988*)

8 Congo red is a stain which binds loosely to molecules of the protein, fibrin to give a red powder. When incubated with a proteolytic enzyme, such as trypsin, the fibrin breaks down. The congo red is released into the solution which turns from clear to red. Broad bean seeds are said to contain a water-soluble substance which inhibits the action of trypsin. Design an experiment to test this hypothesis. In your answer give details of: (a) the method you would use including the control; (b) how you would collect and analyse your results. (10)
(*AEB AS and A-level, 1989*)

9(a) Why is outbreeding an advantage to flowering plants? (2)
(b) The diagram below represents a section through a flower in which there is a special mechanical device which favours outbreeding.
(i) Suggest the sequence of events by which pollen would be transferred on to the body of a visiting insect. (3)

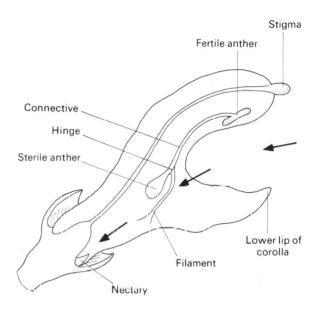

Path taken by visiting insect

(ii) How do the relative positions of the fertile anther and stigma favour outbreeding? (2)
(iii) In this flower the anthers ripen before the stigma becomes receptive. Explain how this favours outbreeding. (2)
(c) Name *one* condition found in certain flowering plants which makes outbreeding inevitable. (1)
(*London A-level, 1988*)

10 The roots of twelve bean plants were immersed in a nutrient solution containing radioactive phosphate (^{32}P) for 24 hours. The plants were then transferred to a non-radioactive nutrient solution and the leaves of six of the plants were covered with aluminium foil to exclude light.
The graph below shows the daily measurements of radioactivity in the leaves in counts per minute (cpm) of unit area.

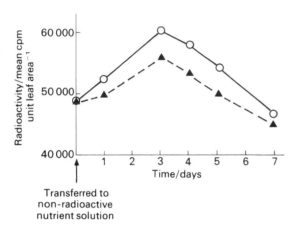

Transferred to
non-radioactive
nutrient solution

○——○ Leaves not covered

▲--▲ Leaves covered

(a) Explain briefly how the ^{32}P passed from the nutrient solution to the leaves. (5)
(b) How would the amount of ^{32}P in the uncovered leaves have been affected if the plants had been exposed to moving air? Give a reason for your answer. (1)
(c) Suggest a reason for the difference in amount of radioactivity in the two sets of leaves. (2)
(d) (i) In which tissue would radioactive phosphorus have been transported out of the leaves? (1)
　　(ii) Outline an experiment which could be carried out to support your answer. (3)
(e) The mass-flow theory to explain translocation in plants proposes that a positive pressure potential is developed by the build up of soluble sugars at a 'source'. Do the results of this experiment provide evidence to support the mass-flow theory? Give a reason for your answer. (2)
(*London A-level Specimen, 1990*)

11 The procedure and results of an experiment on barley seeds are as follows:

Sterile pieces of isolated aleurone layer from barley seeds were placed on sterilised agar gel containing starch. Gibberellic acid, a plant hormone (i.e. *plant growth substance*), was added to some of the plates, as was cycloheximide, a substance known to prevent protein synthesis. The plates were incubated at 25°C for several days. The agar was then flooded with I$_2$/KI solution to test for the presence of starch and the sizes of the clear areas around each piece of seed were recorded. The results are shown in the table. The digestion of the starch in the agar is due to the presence of the enzyme amylase.

		Gibberellic acid	
		Present	**Absent**
Cycloheximide	**Absent**	0 mm²	0 mm²
	Present	260 mm²	0 mm²

Table 9.2 Size of clear area produced (in mm²) in the presence and absence of gibberellic acid and cycloheximide

(a) Why is the enzyme present in a germinating barley seed? (1)
(b) What do these results suggest is the stimulus for the presence of the enzyme? (1)
(c) What do the effects of cycloheximide on the amount of starch digested indicate about the events leading to starch digestion in a germinating barley seed? (3)
(*Oxford AS, 1989*)

12 In an experiment to investigate the cause of apical dominance in shoots, the concentration of three plant growth hormones (i.e. *plant growth substances*) was measured in lateral buds after a number of hours under the different conditions **A**, **B** and **C** shown in the diagrams. The tables below show the results of these measurements, and the response of the lateral bud in each case after being left for several more days.

Summary of experimental conditions:

(a) What is the advantage to the plant of the leading shoot showing apical dominance?　(1)

(b) What evidence is there from these results that auxin produced in the leading part of the shoot is responsible for maintaining apical dominance?　(1)

(c) One theory of apical dominance suggests that the presence of abscisic acid in the lateral bud prevents its development. Would these results support this theory? Give a reason for your answer.　(1)

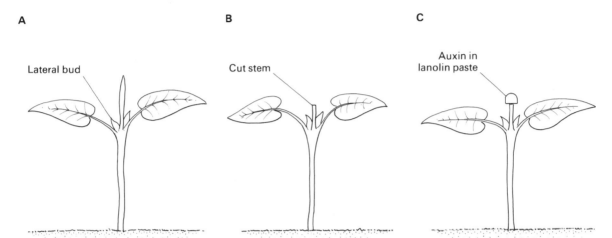

A　　　　　　　　　　　　B　　　　　　　　　　　　C

Lateral bud　　　　　Cut stem　　　　Auxin in lanolin paste

Summary of results:

(d) Explain the changes in the levels of cytokinin. Suggest a possible effect of cytokinin on the lateral bud under natural conditions when the apical bud has been grazed.　(2)

(*Oxford AS, 1989*)

	Levels of hormones in lateral bud		
Hormone	A	B	C
Auxin	High	Low	High
Cytokinin	Low	High	High
Abscisic acid	High	Low	High

Table 9.3

Response of lateral bud		
A	B	C
No growth	Growth	No growth

Table 9.4

13 Two different plants, **X** and **Y**, were exposed to particular patterns of darkness and light for a period of time. The effects of this on the flowering of the plants were recorded. The diagram below represents the length of darkness involved in each case, relative to the known critical night lengths of the plants (this value is arbitrary in the diagram).
(a) Which, if any, of the plants **X** and **Y** is a long day plant? (1)
(b) Suggest a factor other than day length which may influence the time of flowering. (1)
(c) Describe the effect of the red light used in the experiment on the phytochrome found in the leaves of the plants. How does this account for the flowering of plant **X** under condition 3? (3)
(*Oxford AS, 1989*)

Results:

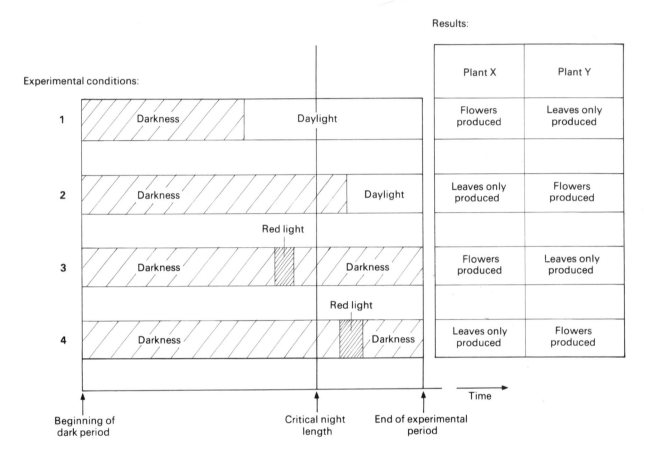

Experimental conditions:

	Plant X	Plant Y
1	Flowers produced	Leaves only produced
2	Leaves only produced	Flowers produced
3	Flowers produced	Leaves only produced
4	Leaves only produced	Flowers produced

14 Explain how a grower would apply his knowledge of the factors limiting growth to the cultivation of a glasshouse crop such as tomatoes. (25)
(*COSSEC AS, 1990*)

15 Explain why some parts of the world suffer from severe food shortages. Discuss the steps that have been taken to overcome these shortages and evaluate their success. (25)
(*COSSEC AS, 1990*)

16 Seeds of cultivated varieties of apple derived from the wild crab-apple have a chilling requirement before they will germinate.

An experiment was carried out to investigate the effect of low temperatures on the breaking of dormancy of apple seeds.

Batches of seeds were kept in moist sand for three months at each of seven different temperatures ranging from −1 to +14°C.

The seeds were then removed and all allowed to germinate at 20°C. The percentage germination for each batch was determined.

The results are shown in the graph opposite.

(a) From the graph, determine the expected percentage germination if the seeds had been exposed to (i) 0°C and (ii) 6°C. (2)

(b) Suggest how the experiment could be modified to find out more accurately the temperature at which the seeds should be stored to give the greatest percentage germination. (2)

(c) (i) Suggest how the results of this experiment relate to what happens to apple seeds in their natural environment. (2)

(ii) Explain why and how an apple breeder could make use of the information gained from this experiment. (2)

(d) Explain one other way in which dormant seeds may be stimulated to germinate. (2)

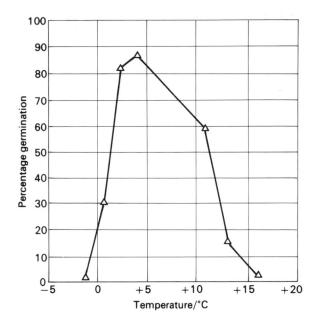

(*London AS, 1990*)

CLASSIFICATION

All organisms can be placed in one of five kingdoms. Plants belong to the kingdom Plantae. (The other kingdoms are Prokaryotae, Protoctista, Fungi and Animalia). A kingdom is the largest taxon (classification group). The other taxa of the plant kingdom are phylum, class, order, family, genus and species. The following are the more important phyla:

• Bryophyta - the mosses (16 000 species) and liverworts (9000 species)

• Sphenophyta - horsetails (40 species)
• Filicinophyta - ferns (12 000 species)
• Coniferophyta - conifers (550 species)
• Angiospermophyta - flowering plants

We are mainly concerned, in this book, with the phylum Angiospermophyta, the flowering plants, which includes more than 230 000 species. It is sub-divided into two classes, monocotyledon and dicotyledon.

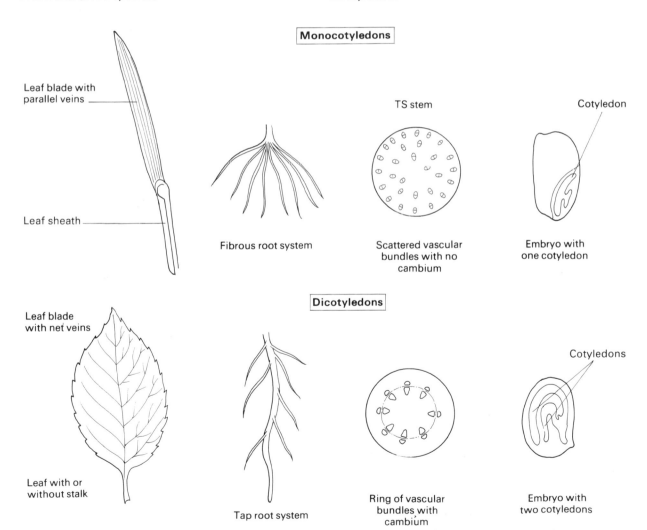

Monocotyledons

Leaf blade with parallel veins

Leaf sheath

Fibrous root system

TS stem

Scattered vascular bundles with no cambium

Cotyledon

Embryo with one cotyledon

Dicotyledons

Leaf blade with net veins

Leaf with or without stalk

Tap root system

Ring of vascular bundles with cambium

Cotyledons

Embryo with two cotyledons

■ RECOGNITION CHARACTERISTICS OF FOUR FAMILIES

■ Monocotyledons

Gramineae: mainly herbs; lanceolate, parallel-veined leaves in two rows with sheathing bases and membraneous ligule at junction of blade and sheath; shoot with swollen nodes (bases of leaf sheaths); flowers wind-pollinated, inconspicuous; flower terminology different from dicotyledons; flowers clustered into spikes bearing glumes and lemmae (bracts) enclosing lodicules (petals and sepals); three stamens and single ovary; fruit dry and shed with some of the bract-like structures. **Examples: cereals and grasses, bamboo, palms**.

■ Dicotyledons

Cruciferae: herbs; leaves spirally arranged on stem; leaves variable - entire or divided without stipules; flowers in branched leafy clusters, radially symmetrical; sepals and petals four, in the form of alternate crosses (cruciform), usually four stamens, parts free (not fused together); fruits 2-valved, usually with vertical central partition, opening from the bottom. **Examples: cabbage, turnip, shepherd's-purse**.

Leguminoseae (Papilionaceae): trees, shrubs or herbs; leaves usually compound with three to many leaflets, with stipules, sometimes with tendrils; flowers bilaterally symmetrical, petals unequal-sized (large standard petal at the back, two wing petals at each side and two fused petals forming a keel in front), joined at the base to form a tube; fruit a pod (legume) with several seeds. **Examples: beans, peas, gorse, laburnum**.

Rosaceae: trees, shrubs or herbs; leaves simple or compound with stipules, arranged alternately on stem, usually with toothed margins; flowers solitary or in spikes or clusters, radially symmetrical, wide open with five free sepals and petals (petals sometimes four or zero), flower parts usually in whorls; stamens five or numerous; fruits varied, dry or fleshy. **Examples: apple, strawberry, rose**. (Rosaceae can be confused with Ranunculaceae (e.g. buttercup) but the latter family has flower parts usually in whorls, the leaves are usually not serrated (toothed) and are usually without stipules.)

APPENDIX 2 BOTANICAL STAINS AND REAGENTS

During the course, you will not only make slides of your own temporary preparations for looking at plant material under the microscope but will also examine permanent, prepared microslides. These notes will help you interpret what you see.

Stains used for temporary preparations
- Methylene blue: stains cytoplasm blue; denser material, such as nuclei, stain a deeper colour.
- Iodine solution: stains starch grains a dark blue-black.
- Phloroglucin: stains lignin a red-brown colour.
- Fabil and Schultz's solution: stains cellulose purple.

Stains used for permanent preparations
- Haematoxylin: stains cytoplasm blue to purple; denser tissue stains a darker colour.

- Light green: stains cytoplasm green.
- Safranin: stains cellulose red.

Other reagents
- 5% Glycerine solution: as a mountant (dries out less quickly than water and material is partially cleared so that it is less opaque).
- 70% Alcohol (Ethanol or purified industrial methanol): fixes (kills) the living parts of cells.
- Benedict's reagent: a test for a reducing sugar; colour change from blue to green, yellow, brick-red.
- Tetrazolium: test for seed viability, colourless to red.
- Cobalt chloride paper: test for water, blue (dry) to pink (wet).